VOCABULARY
IN ACTION

Level C

Reviewers/Consultants

Linda Lott

William McLaughlin

Catherine O'Leary

Elizabeth Pardo

Patricia Walsh

Rosemary Watson

Table of Contents

ACKNOWLEDGMENTS

Managing Editor Margaret O'Leary • **Editors** Kim Mason, Sandy Hazel, Jane Samuelson
Production Project Manager Mary Bowers • **Production** Kari Nicholls, Donna Antkowiak • **Cover Design** Olga Lindsay
ISBN 0-8294-0918-1
© 1997 Loyola Press, 3441 N. Ashland Ave., Chicago, IL 60657 • All rights reserved. • Printed in the United States of America.
BCDEFG 210987

Introduction

Vocabulary in Action is a series of five workbooks, Levels A through E, designed to assess and expand students' vocabulary skills in context. Level C is divided into 15 Chapters. Each Chapter is composed of 20 words with corresponding activities.

Basic Words List

Words were selected based on:

- current everyday language
- usage in textbooks, tradebooks (fiction/nonfiction), magazines
- *The Living Word Vocabulary* for grade placement

Chapters

Each of the fifteen Chapters contains:

- word pronunciations, word meanings, and identifications of parts of speech
- Words in Context and Tell the Story activities that challenge students to determine word usage in the context of a story and sentences
- Synonyms and Antonyms
- Word Study and word building activities that study prefixes, roots, suffixes, analogies, and homonyms
- Fun with Words activity that lets students use the new vocabulary words in an enjoyable context
- Challenge Words that encourage students to expand their vocabulary
- Challenge Writing activity that encourages students to write creatively within a given framework

Assessment

Five Reviews, a Pretest, and a Posttest assess students' prior knowledge and progress by using:

- Word Meanings
- Sentence Completion
- Choosing the Definitions
- Fill in the Blanks
- Classifying Words
- Word Relations
- Using Context Clues
- Analogies

Games & Activities

- reinforces students' vocabulary skills with clever, stimulating activities—used individually or cooperatively

Vocabulary in Action **teaches words in the context of thoughtful, character-building stories.** Plus, it includes your favorite features:

- Fun with Words in each Chapter allows students to use the words in an entertaining, creative activity
- Five extra Challenge Words in each Chapter may be used in a variety of ways: extra credit, the basis for Games & Activities, creative writing assignments, or as additional Chapter words
- Games & Activities reinforces students' vocabulary skills kinesthetically
- Large fonts and long writing lines for easy reading and writing
- Standardized test format at Levels C through E

Pronunciation Key

This key shows the meanings of the abbreviations and symbols used throughout the book.

Some English words have more than one possible pronunciation. This book gives only one pronunciation per word, except when different pronunciations indicate different parts of speech. For example, when the word *relay* is used as a noun, it is pronounced rē´ lā; as a verb, the word is pronounced rə lā´.

Parts of Speech

adj.	adjective	*int.*	interjection	*prep.*	preposition
adv.	adverb	*n.*	noun	*part.*	participle
				v.	verb

Vowels

ā	t<u>a</u>pe	ə	<u>a</u>bout, circ<u>u</u>s	ôr	t<u>or</u>n
a	m<u>a</u>p	ī	k<u>i</u>te	oi	n<u>oi</u>se
âr	st<u>are</u>	i	w<u>i</u>n	ou	f<u>ou</u>l
ä	c<u>ar</u>, f<u>a</u>ther	ō	t<u>oe</u>	o͞o	s<u>oo</u>n
ē	m<u>ee</u>t	o	m<u>o</u>p	o͝o	b<u>oo</u>k
e	k<u>e</u>pt	ô	l<u>a</u>w	u	t<u>u</u>g

Consonants

ch	<u>ch</u>eck	ŋ	ra<u>ng</u>	y	<u>y</u>ellow
g	<u>g</u>irl	th	<u>th</u>imble	zh	trea<u>s</u>ure
j	<u>j</u>am	t̶h̶	<u>th</u>at	sh	<u>sh</u>elf

Stress

The accent mark follows the syllable receiving the major stress, such as in the word *plaster* (plas´ tər).

Pretest

This test contains some of the words you will find in this book. It will give you an idea of the kinds of words you will study. When you have completed all the Chapters, the Posttest will measure what you have learned.

Choosing the Definitions

Fill in the oval next to the item that best defines the boldfaced word in each sentence.

1. On cool evenings, the campers **congregate** around the campfire.
   - a. dance
   - b. gather
   - c. cook
   - d. sing

2. Jack thought a Saturday job would be a **judicious** use of his time.
   - a. wise
   - b. wasteful
   - c. silly
   - d. dangerous

3. Mom stopped the car so everyone could admire the **scenic** view.
   - a. colorful
   - b. ugly
   - c. desert
   - d. attractive

4. Washing dishes is a **tedious** chore.
   - a. exciting
   - b. old
   - c. boring
   - d. brilliant

5. Taking shorter showers **conserves** water.
   - a. drinks
   - b. uses
   - c. saves
   - d. heats

6. The class president will **abstain** from voting if her sister runs for office.
   - a. avoid
   - b. lead
   - c. encourage
   - d. count

7. The flu makes you feel awful, but it is not a **terminal** illness.
   - a. short
   - b. mild
   - c. horrible
   - d. deadly

8. Lying by the warm fire, the old dog gave a sigh of **contentment**.
   - a. sadness
   - b. happiness
   - c. disgust
   - d. exhaustion

9. Swimming across the lake takes a great deal of **stamina**.
   - a. lessons
   - b. speed
   - c. endurance
   - d. nourishment

10. During the earthquake, the statue slid off its **pedestal** and broke.
    - a. hill
    - b. museum
    - c. base
    - d. frame

11. Bess felt a sense of **triumph** after she scored the final goal.
    - a. victory
    - b. defeat
    - c. happiness
    - d. anger

12. The police assured the witness that her name would be kept **confidential**.
    - a. public
    - b. secret
    - c. rewarded
    - d. misspelled

13. Even though it was late, Alan felt an **obligation** to attend the meeting.
    - a. desire
    - b. promise
    - c. duty
    - d. invitation

14. Our canoe ride through the river's rapids was **adventurous.**
    a. dull   b. tiring   c. lengthy   d. risky

15. I **despise** spinach, but I eat it because it's so good for me.
    a. grow   b. hate   c. crave   d. digest

16. Bad-smelling **gaseous** clouds poured out of the factory's smokestack.
    a. solid   b. formless   c. heavy   d. dangerous

17. Vines had grown up to **obscure** the entrance to the abandoned farmhouse.
    a. hide   b. light   c. destroy   d. decorate

18. The **feud** between the two families continued for years.
    a. fence   b. friendship   c. relationship   d. dispute

19. The new police cadets pledged to **uphold** the law.
    a. break   b. write   c. follow   d. learn

20. The room was at the end of a long, dark **corridor.**
    a. road   b. sidewalk   c. tunnel   d. hallway

21. My clever **disguise** even fooled my mom.
    a. answer   b. mask   c. lie   d. outfit

22. Jerry thought the prank was harmless, but it **enraged** his best friend.
    a. angered   b. thrilled   c. scared   d. amused

23. A **horde** of customers waited outside the mall doors at the grand opening.
    a. crowd   b. couple   c. family   d. small group

24. Mickey is a star basketball player, but an **inept** baseball player.
    a. capable   b. better   c. clumsy   d. average

25. Vivian went to the manager's office to **inquire** about the summer job.
    a. complain   b. ask   c. study   d. talk

26. The toddler didn't **shed** a tear when he fell off his tricycle.
    a. cause   b. wipe off   c. pour out   d. hold back

27. Sammy was **appreciative** of his big brother's help.
    a. thankful   b. critical   c. ungrateful   d. bothered

28. We can accomplish the difficult task with hard work and **determination.**
    a. effort   b. speed   c. purpose   d. fear

29. Nadine was **distraught** until her lost dog returned.
    a. satisfied   b. upset   c. encouraged   d. pleased

30. The events that followed were the **consequence** of Jon's angry words.
    (a.) argument　　(b.) beginning　　(c.) work　　(d.) result

31. After making an error in the big game, Angel felt **humiliation** for days.
    (a.) shame　　(b.) joy　　(c.) anger　　(d.) pride

32. The scientist planned to research **marine** life.
    (a.) space　　(b.) desert　　(c.) ground　　(d.) sea

33. Before she could try the recipe, the chef had to **convert** the metric measurements.
    (a.) read　　(b.) change　　(c.) gather　　(d.) test

34. When Rich's cat began behaving **oddly**, he made an appointment with the vet.
    (a.) nicely　　(b.) strangely　　(c.) angrily　　(d.) safely

35. The **shrill** sound of the siren hurt everyone's ears.
    (a.) drawn-out　　(b.) loud　　(c.) high-pitched　　(d.) low

36. Cheri felt it was her **destiny** to become a doctor.
    (a.) future　　(b.) bad luck　　(c.) career　　(d.) ambition

37. The sailors went out in spite of the forecast of **variable** winds.
    (a.) north　　(b.) strong　　(c.) light　　(d.) changeable

38. Mai's feelings were hurt by her parents' **criticism**.
    (a.) description　　(b.) disapproval　　(c.) summary　　(d.) contents

39. When the students worked together, they were able to **generate** more ideas.
    (a.) talk　　(b.) criticize　　(c.) produce　　(d.) destroy

40. In math class, we learned how to measure the **diameter** of a circle.
    (a.) distance around　(b.) weight　　(c.) distance across　(d.) density

41. School was closed for a week because of an **epidemic** of measles.
    (a.) outbreak　　(b.) symptoms　　(c.) vaccine　　(d.) end

42. The sleeping lion looks peaceful, but it can be a **fierce** enemy.
    (a.) tame　　(b.) huge　　(c.) proud　　(d.) cruel

43. Tom thought he would **prevail** over his opponent in the karate match.
    (a.) win　　(b.) throw　　(c.) stand　　(d.) lose

44. I spotted a flaw in the cloth, but it was just a **variation** in its texture.
    (a.) similarity　　(b.) lump　　(c.) difference　　(d.) smoothness

45. At first we thought the puppy's **mischievous** behavior was cute.
    (a.) pleasant　　(b.) naughty　　(c.) affectionate　　(d.) foolish

46. In its early years, people thought the telephone was a **wondrous** invention.
    a. shocking   **b.** frightening   **c.** useful   **d.** amazing

47. We planned a celebration to **commemorate** Mrs. Jarzab's teaching career.
    a. honor   **b.** discredit   **c.** ignore   **d.** write down

48. The book's main character turned out to be a real **scoundrel**.
    a. hero   **b.** villain   **c.** star   **d.** pilot

49. We finally had to tell him that his tasteless jokes made him a **bore**.
    a. woodpecker   **b.** wild pig   **c.** dull person   **d.** comedian

50. The long, hot **drought** ruined the farmers' crops.
    a. storm   **b.** dry spell   **c.** summer   **d.** dirt road

51. Once in a while it's good to take a **solitary** walk to think things over.
    a. brisk   **b.** long   **c.** friendly   **d.** alone

52. I wish my sister would not **gloat** about her grades all the time.
    a. boast   **b.** talk   **c.** whine   **d.** worry

53. After Ashley's description, I had a good **mental** picture of her hometown.
    a. physical   **b.** of the mouth   **c.** masculine   **d.** of the mind

54. The driving instructor told us not to **accelerate** too quickly.
    a. stop   **b.** slow down   **c.** speed up   **d.** drive

55. The sprinkling ban was in effect because of the low level of the **reservoir**.
    a. savings account   **b.** grass   **c.** water supply   **d.** valley

56. We let the gravy **simmer** while we prepared the salad.
    a. thicken   **b.** heat   **c.** stir   **d.** season

57. Before I went on stage, I had a few **qualms** about singing for an audience.
    a. dreams   **b.** songs   **c.** surprises   **d.** worries

58. Our **sturdy** canvas tents kept us dry during the thunderstorm.
    a. strong   **b.** scratchy   **c.** thin   **d.** ugly

59. My mother has a successful career as a jewelry **broker**.
    a. manufacturer   **b.** designer   **c.** model   **d.** salesperson

60. James likes to spend his **leisure** time building models.
    a. class   **b.** free   **c.** work   **d.** evening

61. It was time for the ceremony to **commence**, but the speaker was late.
    a. end   **b.** continue   **c.** begin   **d.** perform

62. The author **dedicated** the book to all the students at King School.
   - (a.) wrote
   - (b.) devoted
   - (c.) read aloud
   - (d.) mailed

63. Babs enjoys using the computer to **correspond** with her friends.
   - (a.) spy
   - (b.) work
   - (c.) play
   - (d.) communicate

64. The club's fund-raising plan **evolved** from one member's casual comment.
   - (a.) turned
   - (b.) discouraged
   - (c.) developed
   - (d.) ended

65. The president received an **ovation** when he stepped up to the microphone.
   - (a.) army
   - (b.) applause
   - (c.) invitation
   - (d.) shock

66. A skunk protects itself with its **abominable** odor.
   - (a.) offensive
   - (b.) fragrant
   - (c.) delightful
   - (d.) strong

67. A **submissive** dog is easily trained.
   - (a.) mean
   - (b.) friendly
   - (c.) large
   - (d.) obedient

68. When his friends knocked, Albie hurried to **conceal** the dirty dishes.
   - (a.) scrub
   - (b.) hide
   - (c.) throw away
   - (d.) show off

69. Waves caused by a hurricane can be even more **destructive** than the wind.
   - (a.) beautiful
   - (b.) powerful
   - (c.) creative
   - (d.) damaging

70. Beavers **gnaw** on trees until they fall.
   - (a.) scrape
   - (b.) kick
   - (c.) chew
   - (d.) break

71. The accident was caused by a **negligent** worker.
   - (a.) well-trained
   - (b.) tired
   - (c.) careless
   - (d.) serious

72. The principal promised to **consider** the new rule.
   - (a.) think about
   - (b.) carry out
   - (c.) enforce
   - (d.) overturn

73. The accountant was able to **swindle** her trusting business partners.
   - (a.) praise
   - (b.) leave
   - (c.) work for
   - (d.) cheat

74. Each class sent a **delegate** to the school meeting.
   - (a.) gathering
   - (b.) representative
   - (c.) vote
   - (d.) speaker

75. Erik made a **gruesome** mask to wear in the play.
   - (a.) gorgeous
   - (b.) frightening
   - (c.) new
   - (d.) artistic

76. The graph showed a **gradual** increase in grocery prices.
   - (a.) large
   - (b.) expected
   - (c.) slow
   - (d.) sudden

77. During World War II, some countries remained **neutral**.
   - (a.) uninvolved
   - (b.) wealthy
   - (c.) angry
   - (d.) unfair

78. The new student seemed **timid** until we got to know her.
    a. nasty   **b.** shy   **c.** unhappy   **d.** intelligent

79. **Technical** books about computers are often difficult to understand.
    a. simple   **b.** long   **c.** scientific   **d.** expensive

80. His father warned Tony not to **trifle** with his little brother's feelings.
    a. wrestle   **b.** treat carelessly   **c.** discuss   **d.** argue with

81. Trudi needs time to **recuperate** from the accident, but she will be fine.
    a. get sick   **b.** sleep   **c.** get well   **d.** run

82. The colonists decided it was time to **rebel** against the unfair government.
    a. reject authority   **b.** obey authority   **c.** celebrate   **d.** pay taxes

83. In solving the conflict, Josie displayed a real talent for **persuasion.**
    a. giving speeches   **b.** writing essays   **c.** convincing   **d.** fighting

84. Our new neighbor's **jovial** smile gave us a clue to his personality.
    a. sinister   **b.** nervous   **c.** shy   **d.** merry

85. Our class wrote a letter about the problem to the town **council.**
    a. mayor   **b.** city hall   **c.** treasurer   **d.** board of advisors

86. We didn't realize that the window was **ajar** until we felt a cold draft.
    a. broken   **b.** dirty   **c.** open   **d.** locked

87. No matter what we did, we could not make the poster **adhere** to the wall.
    a. cling   **b.** fall off   **c.** look good   **d.** draw

88. When the electricity shut down, the emergency **generator** saved the day.
    a. employee   **b.** director   **c.** power supply   **d.** rescue team

89. The **geologist** who explored the sea valley brought up some rare specimens.
    a. submarine   **b.** animal scientist   **c.** rock scientist   **d.** mapmaker

90. Harry was voted the best **scholar** in the class.
    a. artist   **b.** athlete   **c.** teacher   **d.** student

## Chapter 1

Word List

Read each word using the pronunciation key.

Basic Words

abominable (ə bom´ ə nə bəl)
angle (aŋ´ gəl)
athlete (ath´ lēt)
calorie (kal´ ə rē)
congregate (koŋ´ gri gāt)
denounce (di nouns´)
disbelief (dis bi lēf´)
elusive (i lōō´ siv)
explosion (ik splō´ zhən)
feud (fyōōd)
granite (gran´ it)
illicit (i lis´ it)
judicious (jōō dish´ əs)
mischievous (mis´ chə vəs)
parody (pâr´ ə dē)
pupil (pyōō´ pəl)
reveal (ri vēl´)
slogan (slō´ gən)
tendon (ten´ dən)
vibrate (vī´ brāt)

Challenge Words

adjacent (ə jā´ sənt)
customary (kus´ tə mâr ē)
fickle (fik´ əl)
legacy (le´ gə sē)
proficient (prə fish´ ənt)

Word Study

Suffixes

The suffix *-ful* means *full of.*

careful (kâr´ fəl) *(adj.)* full of care or concern
graceful (grās´ fəl) *(adj.)* having grace
peaceful (pēs´ fəl) *(adj.)* full of peace; quiet
powerful (pou´ ər fəl) *(adj.)* full of power
successful (sək ses´ fəl) *(adj.)* having success
thoughtful (thôt´ fəl) *(adj.)* full of thought; thinking

Be Careful!

Commonly Misspelled Words

beginning	grabbed	swimming
myself	basketball	themselves

# Words in Context

Read each sentence below to decipher the meaning of each boldface word. Use reasoning skills and the remainder of the sentence to help you. Write the meaning of the word on the line.

1. Denise, a natural **athlete**, ran every day to prepare for the marathon.

   _____

2. The detective uncovered the criminal's **illicit** activities and arrested him.

   _____

3. The sudden **explosion** at the factory blew out the windows and doors.

   _____

4. Where will we **congregate** before the concert so we can go in together?

   _____

5. Did Jeff **reveal** his identity before the masquerade party?

   _____

6. The courthouse steps are made of **granite** from an Alabama rock quarry.

   _____

7. When hiking in the hot, dry desert, a careful and **judicious** use of water is necessary.

   _____

8. Can we settle our disagreement without a long family **feud?**

   _____

9. My **mischievous** sister played a practical joke on me.

   _____

10. I need a good, catchy **slogan** to write on my campaign posters.

   _____

Word Meanings

Within each group, study the spelling, part(s) of speech, and meaning(s) of each word. Complete each sentence by writing the word on the line. Then read the sentence.

Basic Words

1. **abominable** *(adj.)* 1. offensive; 2. unpleasant

   Can someone stop that screaming child's _____ behavior?

2. **angle** *(n.)* the space between two surfaces or lines that meet *(v.)* to bend at an angle

   Each corner of a square is a right _____ .

   If you _____ the ladder more toward the house, it will reach the roof.

3. **athlete** *(n.)* a person trained or skilled in a sport

   Which sports figure was named as the year's best _____ ?

4. **calorie** *(n.)* a unit used to measure the energy supplied by food

   That diet drink has only one _____ ?

5. **congregate** *(v.)* to group together into a crowd

   The early students always _____ at the school's entrance.

6. **denounce** *(v.)* to strongly speak out against someone or something

   Our committee will appear before Congress to _____ television violence.

7. **disbelief** *(n.)* reluctance or refusal to believe

   "Looks like a UFO," the agent said, staring at the sky in _____ .

8. **elusive** *(adj.)* difficult to describe or understand

   Storytellers say there's an _____ fragrance around the old, abandoned factory.

9. **explosion** *(n.)* 1. a loud blast; 2. a blowing up

   Smoking rubble was all that remained after the sudden _____ .

10. **feud** *(n.)* 1. an extended and bitter quarrel between families; 2. an extreme hatred between people or groups *(v.)* to carry on a violent quarrel over an extended period of time

The _____ over land continued for generations.

Do you think the sisters will _____ over possession of the hair dryer?

11. **granite** *(n.)* a light-colored, hard rock, usually pink or gray

The new park statue is made of _____ from these hills.

12. **illicit** *(adj.)* 1. unauthorized; 2. unlawful; 3. illegal

Security officers detected the _____ activity of the managers.

13. **judicious** *(adj.)* 1. sensible; 2. wise; 3. having or using good judgment

The mayor's _____ actions avoided an embarrassing mistake.

14. **mischievous** *(adj.)* 1. causing mischief, naughty; 2. harmful; 3. prankish

The court jester's _____ deeds did not please the king.

15. **parody** *(n.)* a comical interpretation of a musical or literary work

Bernie's _____ of a familiar song got us all laughing.

16. **pupil** *(n.)* the area in the center of the eye that is black

The special eyedrops caused my _____ to enlarge.

17. **reveal** *(v.)* 1. to make known; 2. to disclose; 3. to publicize or broadcast

The celebrity announcer will _____ the $10,000 winner during the football game.

18. **slogan** *(n.)* an attention-getting word or phrase used by a business, political party, or group

"The incredible edible egg" is a catchy _____ .

19. **tendon** *(n.)* a strong band of tissue in the body that joins muscle to bone

The pitcher pulled a leg _____ and won't be playing today.

20. **vibrate** *(v.)* to move quickly back and forth

We could feel the roller coaster shake and _____ as we rounded the curve.

Challenge Words

adjacent *(adj.)* 1. having a common border; 2. directly preceding or following

Room 201 and Room 202 are _____ rooms.

customary *(adj.)* commonly practiced or used

Every morning I eat my _____ bowl of cereal and fruit.

fickle *(adj.)* 1. easily gives in to change; 2. lacks consistency

I seem to have _____ friends who change their minds all the time.

legacy *(n.)* something received from an ancestor

My love for African history is part of the _____ of my Great-Uncle Malik.

proficient *(adj.)* having competence and skill in a specific area

Michael Jordan is a _____ basketball player.

Synonyms

Synonyms are words that have the same or nearly the same meanings.

Part 1 Choose the word from the box that is the synonym for each group of words. Write the word on the line.

athlete	explosion	congregate	feud
reveal	illicit	disbelief	judicious

1. to tell, announce, expose, unveil _____

2. criminal, wrong, outside the law _____

3. to assemble, collect, draw together _____

4. a dispute, fight; to argue, battle _____

5. an eruption, outburst, discharge _____

6. sound, rational, reasonable _____

7. doubt, suspicion

_____

8. someone trained in sports,
   a physically fit person

_____

Part 2 Replace the underlined word(s) with a word from the Basic Words list that means the same or almost the same thing. Write your answer on the line.

9. His silent, <u>hard-to-understand</u> brother never eats with the family.

_____

10. That <u>tricky</u> squirrel got into the bird feeder once again. _____

11. Marc pulled over when the steering wheel began to <u>shake</u>. _____

12. Sarah expected the boys to be <u>horrible</u> dancers, but they weren't.

_____

13. Choose your words carefully when you <u>attack</u> your campaign opponent's

viewpoint. _____

14. The comedy show was one television commercial <u>imitation</u> after another.

_____

15. Jim can't get that car dealer's <u>jingle</u> out of his head. _____

Antonyms

Antonyms are words that have opposite or nearly opposite meanings.

Part 1 Choose the word from the box that is the antonym for each group of words. Write the word on the line.

elusive	congregate	vibrate	judicious	denounce

1. to disperse, leave, scatter _____

2. clear, well known, easy to define _____

3. to praise, support, approve _____

4. silly, foolish, senseless _____

5. to be still, motionless, at rest _____

Part 2 Replace the underlined word(s) with a word from the Basic Words list that means the opposite or almost the opposite thing. Write your answer on the line.

6. "Look! I got an A on my reading test," Florence said with <u>confidence</u>.

_____

7. The twins <u>get along well</u> all the time, and this astonishes their parents.

_____

8. My aunt sent me the most <u>attractive</u> orange skirt I have ever seen.

_____

9. In some states, burning autumn leaves is <u>legal</u>. _____

10. The news reporter plans to <u>conceal</u> harmful information. _____

Word Study/Suffixes

Write the word from the box that has the same meaning as the first word and the suffix *-ful*.

powerful	graceful	peaceful
successful	careful	thoughtful

1. concern + ful _____

2. quiet + ful _____

3. idea + ful

_____

4. beauty of movement + ful

_____

5. strength + ful

_____

6. fortune + ful

_____

 # Challenge Writing

The Search An ancestor of yours has left a large trunk buried somewhere. You find a map, follow it, and uncover the trunk. On a separate sheet of paper, write an account of your search for an adventure magazine. Use the Challenge Words below. Be sure to tell where you went and what you found when the trunk was finally opened. But first, brainstorm for ideas and then write them in the space below.

adjacent	customary	fickle	legacy	proficient

_____

_____

_____

_____

_____

_____

_____

_____

Tell the Story

Choose the word from the Basic Words list that best completes each sentence. Write the word on the line. You may use the plural form of nouns and the past tense of verbs if necessary.

This morning, as I was eating a low-fat breakfast of 70 __1__ , my father __2__ his special, secret plan for our family. At first he gave only __3__ hints that we didn't understand. "I have made a wise, __4__ decision that I think you will like," Dad claimed. "To avoid the yearly __5__ over our vacation plans, I have made the arrangements."

My sister and I looked at each other in __6__ . Usually, we discussed plans before arrangements were made. "Before you speak to __7__ the plans, listen first," Dad said. "I have not used our vacation money in any wrongful or __8__ way," he teased. "To begin, we will all __9__ at a large building made of gray __10__ just outside of our city. We will walk long distances in this building, so we'll need to stretch our leg __11__ like a(n) __12__ to get into good, physical shape.

"Outside of the building are straight roadways that form __13__ . The roadways are for vehicles that often __14__ and shake as they take off, but our takeoff will be gentle and nearly silent. We'll be in our own Friendly Skies, to quote a well-known __15__ ." He sang a quick, funny __16__ of the song "Up, up and away in my beautiful balloon."

"It sounds like an awful, __17__ beginning to our vacation," my sister groaned.

"Dad, stop your __18__ teasing!" I said. "You're talking about the airport."

The __19__ of my sister's eyes grew larger as she realized that there might be more to this vacation than she thought. "Yes," said Dad. "We're going to the airport for a journey in a hot air balloon." The silence in the room was like the silence that follows a loud __20__ . Then we cheered.

1. _____

2. _____

3. _____

4. _____

5. _____

6. _____

7. _____

8. _____

9. _____

10. _____

11. _____

12. _____

13. _____

14. _____

15. _____

16. _____

17. _____

18. _____

19. _____

20. _____

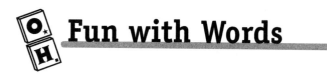 # Fun with Words

Unscramble the letters to form chapter words. Write the word on the line. Then use the word in a sentence.

1. elabinboam

   _____

_____

2. citilli

   _____

_____

3. ceategrong

   _____

_____

4. lahette

   _____

_____

5. nosepliox

   _____

_____

6. naglos

   _____

_____

7. laeiroc

   _____

_____

8. learve

   _____

_____

9. bratvei

   _____

_____

10. esevilu

   _____

_____

## Chapter 2

Word List

Read each word using the pronunciation key.

Basic Words

abstain (ab stān´)
annex (an´ eks)
candidate (kan´ də dāt)
commit (kə mit´)
consequence (kon´ sə kwens)
constellation (kon stə lā´ shən)
depict (di pikt´)
discontent (dis kən tent´)
emigrate (em´ i grāt)
fierce (fērs)
grovel (grov´ əl)
impact (im´ pakt)
juvenile (jōō´ və nīl)
misfit (mis´ fit)
perch (pərch)
qualm (kwäm)
smolder (smōl´ dər)
tedious (tē´ dē əs)
tension (ten´ shən)
vital (vīt´ əl)

Challenge Words

alliance (ə lī´ əns)
fluster (flus´ tər)
infamous (in´ fə məs)
misdemeanor (mis də mē´ nər)
turmoil (tər´ moil)

Word Study

Prefixes

The prefix *dis-* means *not* or *the absence of*.

disadvantage (dis əd van´ tij) *(n.)* lack of advantage
disagree (dis ə grē´) *(v.)* to not agree
discomfort (dis kum´ fərt) *(n.)* lack of comfort
discontinue (dis kən tin´ yü) *(v.)* to stop; to not continue
disgrace (dis grās´) *(n.)* loss of honor
disobey (dis ə bā) *(v.)* to not conform; to not follow commands

Be Careful!

Commonly Misspelled Words

business	cough	through
bargain	usually	fragile

 # Words in Context

Read each sentence below to decipher the meaning of each boldface word. Use reasoning skills and the remainder of the sentence to help you. Write the meaning of the word on the line.

1. Are you going to be a **candidate** in our school election?

   _____

2. The head-on **impact** crumpled the bumpers and hoods of both cars.

   _____

3. Because of a knee injury, I must **abstain** from jogging for one year.

   _____

4. When did your ancestors **emigrate** from Japan to the United States?

   _____

5. Vultures often **perch** in treetops as they watch for prey.

   _____

6. The astronomer pointed out the **constellation** of Orion in the night sky.

   _____

7. The weather forecaster warned of the hurricane's **fierce** winds.

   _____

8. My four-year-old brother made a beeline to the library's collection of **juvenile** books.

   _____

9. It's hard to choose when I have **qualms** about both summer camps.

   _____

10. Is it wise to let the campfire **smolder** after we've gone to bed?

   _____

Word Meanings

Within each group, study the spelling, part(s) of speech, and meaning(s) of each word. Complete each sentence by writing the word on the line. Then read the sentence.

Basic Words

1. **abstain** *(v.)* to do without

   The doctor told Liz to _____ from all milk products until she feels better.

2. **annex** *(n.)* 1. a part that is added; 2. an added part to a building

   Mr. March's office is located next door, in our building's _____.

3. **candidate** *(n.)* a person who desires to be elected to some office or honor

   The presidential _____ will visit our school just before the election.

4. **commit** *(v.)* 1. to involve or pledge oneself; 2. to be bound to do

   The project leader wanted only people who could _____ to the full two weeks.

5. **consequence** *(n.)* a result of one's actions

   If Ralph didn't follow the rule, then he should expect the _____.

6. **constellation** *(n.)* a grouping of stars that forms a pattern

   Dan looks for the three stars in a row to find his favorite _____.

7. **depict** *(v.)* to portray by picture or word

   The artist pondered how to _____ honesty and grace in the princess's portrait.

8. **discontent** *(adj.)* 1. unhappy; 2. displeased; 3. dissatisfied *(n.)* unhappiness or dissatisfaction

   The workers were _____ with their low wages.

   The _____ of the workers could lead to a bitter strike.

9. **emigrate** *(v.)* to move from one's own country to live in another

   Who will be the next to _____ from Russia to Israel?

10. **fierce** *(adj.)* 1. intense; 2. wild; 3. furious

The _____ look of the lionfish scares away predators.

11. **grovel** *(v.)* 1. to creep at someone's feet; 2. to humble oneself

Duke and Lady _____ when they have been bad dogs.

12. **impact** *(n.)* 1. a collision of one thing against another; 2. a striking

The _____ of the huge tree hitting the ground shook the entire forest.

13. **juvenile** *(n.)* a young person *(adj.)* of or for children

Here is a book about a sixth-grade boy suitable for a _____ to read.

Playing silly practical jokes is _____ behavior.

14. **misfit** *(n.)* a person who is not suited for a particular job or group

Being all thumbs, I was a _____ in wood shop class.

15. **perch** *(v.)* to rest or settle in a high place or on an insecure surface

Our binoculars enabled us to see an eagle _____ in the tall tree.

16. **qualm** *(n.)* a sudden uneasiness or doubtfulness of the mind

Rob has no _____ about asking for help when he needs it.

17. **smolder** *(v.)* to burn and smoke without flame

You can put the fire out now or allow it to _____ for awhile.

18. **tedious** *(adj.)* 1. boring; 2. tiring

Lila took over the _____ job of sewing on each and every button.

19. **tension** *(n.)* 1. the stress that results from stretching; 2. a strain

The sail went up as we increased the _____ on the ropes.

20. **vital** *(adj.)* 1. essential; 2. critical

Jesse's leadership and good sense make her a _____ part of our team.

Challenge Words

alliance *(n.)* bond or connection between countries, parties, or persons

Kate and Alicia formed an _____ when they pledged to always be friends.

fluster *(v.)* to make very confused and bothered

Driving and parking a car _____ me so much that I take the train.

infamous *(adj.)* having a bad reputation

The _____ outlaw Jesse James was not welcome in this town.

misdemeanor *(n.)* less serious crime than a felony

Parking illegally is a _____ , while kidnapping is a felony.

turmoil *(n.)* the condition of extreme confusion or agitation

The swarm of angry bees caused a great _____ at the picnic.

Synonyms

Synonyms are words that have the same or nearly the same meanings.

Part 1 Choose the word from the box that is the synonym for each group of words. Write the word on the line.

fierce	abstain	discontent	consequence
commit	vital	qualm	tedious

1. untamed, cruel, extreme   _____

2. to bind, obligate   _____

3. dull, humdrum, uninteresting   _____

4. to avoid, give up, not use   _____

5. important, necessary, required   _____

6. an outcome, effect, product   _____

7. a worry, misgiving, dread _____

8. sadness, restlessness; troubled _____

Part 2 Replace the underlined word(s) with a word from the Basic Words list that means the same or almost the same thing. Write your answer on the line.

9. The <u>expansion</u> will house 16 new offices for extra staff members.

_____

10. There's a ledge in the henhouse where the hens can <u>roost</u>. _____

11. A promise of a better life causes many families to <u>relocate</u> to new places.

_____

12. The <u>smashing</u> of the logs at the bottom of the slide sent up a big spray of water.

_____

13. How would you <u>characterize</u> President Clinton's first four years in office?

_____

14. Kids in trouble appear in <u>youth</u> court. _____

15. You need to increase the <u>tightness</u> on the strings to tune your guitar.

_____

Antonyms

Antonyms are words that have opposite or nearly opposite meanings.

Part 1 Choose the word from the box that is the antonym for each group of words. Write the word on the line.

fierce	abstain	qualm
misfit	tension	juvenile

1. an older person; relating to adults _____

2. a person who is accepted _____

3. calm, meek, mild, tame _____

4. to take part in something _____

5. lack of stress, relaxation _____

6. lack of doubt, security _____

Part 2 Replace the underlined word(s) with a word from the Basic Words list that means the opposite or almost the opposite thing. Write your answer on the line.

7. The political troubles influenced the man's decision to <u>stay in one place</u>.

_____

8. The diplomat was unaware that he presented <u>useless</u> information.

_____

9. Don't you agree that the TV show on the life cycle of the aphid is <u>interesting</u>?

_____

10. The paper in the wastebasket began to <u>blaze</u>. _____

11. The bright color of these walls adds to my <u>pleasure</u>. _____

Word Study/Prefixes

Write the word from the box that has the prefix *dis-* and the same meaning as the next word or words that follow.

disobey	disagree	discomfort
disadvantage	disgrace	discontinue

1. dis + favorable _____

2. dis + get along _____

3. dis + listen to _____

4. dis + freedom from strain _____

5. dis + go on with _____

6. dis + charm _____

Tell the Story

Choose the word from the Basic Words list that best completes each sentence. Write the word on the line. You may use the plural form of nouns and the past tense of verbs if necessary.

Our neighbors __1__ to the United States from another country. They were __2__ with the living conditions in their native country and were __3__ in their determination to find a better life. Even today, they tell stories that __4__ how difficult life in their country was. They remember that if homes caught on fire, families could only watch the remains __5__ because often there was no water. Armed soldiers would __6__ on rooftops just to show who was in control. Citizens had to __7__ from criticizing their government, or they would face harsh __8__. Political __9__ caused neighbors to quarrel and accuse each other.

The long and __10__ process to get permission to leave could take years. Sometimes the only way to get permission was to __11__ and beg. Volunteers __12__ much of their time to help families become __13__ for emigration. Those who wanted to leave would first live with several other people in a small __14__ attached to the village church.

Even after our neighbors received permission to emigrate, they had __15__ about their choice — it was hard to leave family and friends behind. They were comforted by gazing at the stars in the night sky knowing they would see the same __16__ in their new country. When it came time to leave, each person could only pack a few __17__ items. The __18__ of two ways of life colliding made it difficult for our neighbors to adjust at first. Sometimes they felt like __19__ because they didn't speak any English. The elderly members of the family had the most difficulty getting used to things, but the __20__ members felt at home in just a few months.

1. _____

2. _____

3. _____

4. _____

5. _____

6. _____

7. _____

8. _____

9. _____

10. _____

11. _____

12. _____

13. _____

14. _____

15. _____

16. _____

17. _____

18. _____

19. _____

20. _____

Challenge Writing

A Strange Planet You are a space traveler. You and your crew have just landed on a planet inhabited by people whose language and customs are strange to you. Write a diary entry describing your first day on this planet. Use the Challenge Words below. Describe the landscape and people. Tell about any difficulties you encountered.

alliance	fluster	infamous	misdemeanor	turmoil

_____

_____

_____

_____

_____

_____

_____

_____

_____

_____

_____

_____

_____

_____

_____

_____

_____

_____

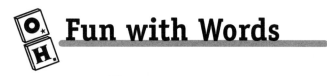# Fun with Words

It is the year 2029. Your pen pal Malpropo, who lives on Xanfor 12, has sent you a message on the interspace network. Malpropo's English is not perfect, so you need to figure out the message in a few places. Cross out the words that are incorrect and replace them with the correct vocabulary words from this chapter.

Greetings, friend!

I have great news. Last week I discovered

a new conversation of thirteen stars. I wish I

could depress for you the way it looks in our

sky. I'm so happy now— all my feelings of

discount are gone. I no longer think of myself

as a mister in my group. In fact, Darnag told me

I am a vitamin part of the project. I have decided

not to emerald to Xanfor 13, but I would like to

visit you on Earth. Write soon.

Malpropo

## Chapter 3

Word List

Read each word using the pronunciation key.

Basic Words

accelerate (ak sel´ ə rāt)
captivity (kap tiv´ ə tē)
conserve (kən sərv´)
despair (di spâr´)
disguise (dis gīz´)
enamel (i nam´ əl)
exotic (eg zot´ ic)
figurative (fig´ yər ə tiv)
gruesome (grōō´ səm)
implement (im´ plə mənt)
keen (kēn)
mismanage (mis man´ ij)
notation (nō tā´ shən)
perishable (per´ i shə bəl)
procedure (pro sē´ jər)
quench (kwench)
savage (sav´ ij)
sneer (snēr)
terminal (tər´ mə nəl)
vocation (vō cā´ shən)

Challenge Words

amiss (ə mis´)
dissuade (di swād´)
futile (fyōō´ təl)
meager (mē´ gər)
prudent (prōōd´ ənt)

Word Study

Homonyms

Homonyms are words that have the same pronunciation, but different meanings.

chili (chil´ ē) *(n.)* a hot-tasting pod of red pepper
chilly (chil´ ē) *(adj.)* unpleasantly cool

canvas (kan´ vəs) *(n.)* firmly woven cloth usually of cotton or linen
canvass (kan´ vəs) *(v.)* 1. to examine in detail; 2 to go to an area to try and get votes for a candidate

overseas (ō ´ vər sē´) *(adv.)* across the sea
oversees (ō vər sēz´) *(v.)* supervises

Be Careful!

Commonly Misspelled Words

doesn't	judgment	balloon
guarantee	again	except

 # Words in Context

Read each sentence below to decipher the meaning of each boldface word. Use reasoning skills and the remainder of the sentence to help you. Write the meaning of the word on the line.

1. We need to establish a **procedure** for ending our club meetings.

_____

2. Please put the **perishable** food in the refrigerator so it won't spoil.

_____

3. A tall glass of cold lemonade can **quench** your thirst on a hot day.

_____

4. Farm **implements**, including tractors and plows, will be sold at the auction.

_____

5. Because of the drought, we are all expected to **conserve** water.

_____

6. What clever **disguise** will you wear to the costume party?

_____

7. The **gruesome** lizardlike creature in the movie disgusted me.

_____

8. Julie was in a state of **despair** over the loss of her grandmother's ring.

_____

9. I am careful not to **mismanage** my savings so that I'll have money when I need it.

_____

10. To someone raised in a rural town, the food in Thailand might seem **exotic**.

_____

Word Meanings

Within each group, study the spelling, part(s) of speech, and meaning(s) of each word. Complete each sentence by writing the word on the line. Then read the sentence.

Basic Words

1. **accelerate** *(v.)* to increase speed

   The minivan needed to _____ to pass the truck on the highway.

2. **captivity** *(n.)* the condition of being held against one's will

   Many zoos use natural settings instead of caged _____.

3. **conserve** *(v.)* 1. to preserve; 2. to keep from being used up

   Recycling is one way to _____ Earth's natural resources.

4. **despair** *(n.)* 1. hopelessness; 2. discouragement *(v.)* to lose all faith or hope

   The assassination of the president left the country in _____.

   Don't _____, the football game isn't over yet.

5. **disguise** *(n.)* a mask or cover-up *(v.)* to mask or conceal one's appearance so as to look like someone else

   Betty needs a clever _____ so that no one will recognize her.

   Wallace will _____ himself as a clown.

6. **enamel** *(n.)* a surface or outer covering that has a smooth, glossy appearance *(v.)* to cover or decorate with a smooth, glossy covering

   This toothpaste will help to whiten the _____ of your teeth.

   The art teacher showed us how to _____ our clay pots.

7. **exotic** *(adj.)* 1. strange; 2. foreign; 3. unknown

   The newly retired couple was ready for an _____ vacation.

8. **figurative** *(adj.)* using words or phrases to mean something different than their usual meaning

   To say that the snow is a feather comforter over the fields is a

   _____ description.

9. **gruesome** *(adj.)* 1. hideous; 2. causing terror or fear

   A _____ main character might insure the movie's success.

10. **implement** *(n.)* a tool, instrument, or utensil

    The dentist used an _____ that looked like a toothpick.

11. **keen** *(adj.)* quick, sharp, enthusiastic

    Quiz show contestants are rewarded for their _____ minds.

12. **mismanage** *(v.)* to control or handle poorly

    John can buy a snowboard if he doesn't _____ his money.

13. **notation** *(n.)* a brief written record

    You'll find the source of the _____ at the end of the book.

14. **perishable** *(adj.)* 1. capable of decaying; 2. biodegradable; 3. decomposable

    The _____ foods will be shipped in a refrigerated truck.

15. **procedure** *(n.)* 1. plan; 2. a way of doing something

    Please read the _____ for emergencies.

16. **quench** *(v.)* 1. to satisfy; 2. to put out or extinguish

    Martha used baking soda to _____ the grease fire on the stove.

17. **savage** *(adj.)* 1. fierce; 2. wild; 3. cruel

    Disney's *The Lion King* creates lovable characters from _____ beasts.

18. **sneer** *(n.)* a look or words that express scorn *(v.)* 1. to show scorn by looks or words; 2. to taunt

    The young, rebellious actor James Dean was a master of the _____.

    The referee considers it unsportsmanlike when players _____ at rivals.

19. **terminal** *(n.)* 1. the end; 2. end part; 3. a freight or passenger train station *(adj.)* 1. fatal; 2. deadly

    Terry departed the train at the _____.

    Strep throat is no longer a _____ disease as it was before the discovery of penicillin.

20. **vocation** *(n.)* a person's occupation or business. She felt her _____ was to manage a homeless shelter.

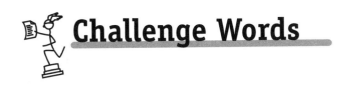

Challenge Words

amiss *(adj.)* 1. not in the right order; 2. out of place

I knew something was _____ when I saw the broken dish on the floor.

dissuade *(v.)* to advise against something

I tried to _____ them against driving on the icy road.

futile *(adj.)* 1. not producing; 2. vain; 3. useless

He made one more _____ attempt and gave up.

meager *(adj.)* deficient in quality and/or strength

A basketball team with only four players is _____ in numbers.

prudent *(adj.)* marked by great wisdom or good judgment

A _____ person always carries an umbrella on rainy days.

Synonyms

Synonyms are words that have the same or nearly the same meanings.

Part 1 Choose the word from the box that is the synonym for each group of words. Write the word on the line.

disguise	notation	conserve	implement
gruesome	accelerate	captivity	vocation

1. a job, craft, career _____

2. a costume; to hide, obscure _____

3. a comment, message, writing _____

4. to hurry, advance, go faster _____

5. to protect, save, guard _____

6. frightful, grim, scary _____

7. lack of freedom, imprisonment _____

8. a piece of equipment _____

Part 2 Replace the underlined word(s) with a word from the Basic Words list that means the same or almost the same thing. Write your answer on the line.

9. "Get that <u>scornful look</u> off your face," the policeman said to the thief.

_____

10. The campers showed a <u>spirited</u> interest in learning rock climbing.

_____

11. The tigers in the circus act have never been <u>ferocious</u> beasts. _____

12. The ushers need to keep control and not <u>mess up</u> the crowd. _____

13. Grant Hospital's emergency room <u>program</u> is a model for other hospitals.

_____

14. The new teacher is the first to <u>fulfill</u> Ryan's thirst for knowledge.

_____

15. The beginning of the school year may be difficult, but don't <u>give up</u>.

_____

Antonyms

Antonyms are words that have opposite or nearly opposite meanings.

Part 1 Choose the word from the box that is the antonym for each group of words. Write the word on the line.

captivity	mismanage	perishable	savage	conserve

1. to waste, destroy, throw away _____

2. to take care of properly _____

3. freedom, independence, liberty _____

4. tamed, gentle, kind _____

5. lasting, not easily spoiled _____

Part 2 Replace the underlined word(s) with a word from the Basic Words list that means the opposite or almost the opposite thing. Write your answer on the line.

6. Dave's comments reveal the extent of his <u>dull</u> wit. _____

7. I think this room needs an <u>ordinary</u> rug to go with the oriental wallpaper.

_____

8. Time seems to <u>slow down</u> as the clock nears 3 P.M. _____

9. At the particularly <u>pleasing</u> part of the play, several people walked out.

_____

10. You'll find your luggage at the <u>starting point</u>. _____

Word Study/Homonyms

Choose the homonym that correctly completes each sentence. Write the word on the line.

1. We'll cook up a big pot of (chilly, chili) for the soccer fans. _____

2. The shirt you are wearing is very thick; it must be made of (canvass, canvas).

_____

3. The unseasonably (chilly, chili) weather might discourage visitors.

_____

4. The Language Club will go (overseas, oversees) to study French for three weeks.

_____

5. I am going to (canvass, canvas) the hallways looking for my lost locker key.

_____

6. Who (overseas, oversees) the cafeteria at lunchtime? _____

Tell the Story

Choose the word from the Basic Words list that best completes each sentence. Write the word on the line. You may use the plural form of nouns and the past tense of verbs if necessary.

My cousin's chosen __1__ is working as a conservationist in Africa. He keeps a journal of scientific __2__ about the animals he sees. He also records each day's __3__ in order to improve the way he observes animals. In addition, he composes poetry and uses beautiful __4__ language to describe the beauty of the land around him.

The tan safari clothes he wears help to __5__ him so that the animals don't notice him. He got too close to a rhinoceros once and had to __6__ his vehicle to escape. He narrowly saved himself from a(n) __7__, gory end. Not all animals are __8__ beasts, though. Many are just curious, like the monkeys who stole his utensils and cooking __9__. He's certain that the sassy monkeys __10__ as they made off with his glossy, new __11__ pots and pans.

Life in central Africa is difficult but not __12__. It's important to not __13__ your food. You don't want to run out, and you don't want __14__ food to spoil. Also, you must carry clean water to __15__ your thirst after a long hike.

My cousin cannot stand to see animals held in __16__, yet he feels __17__ for the disappearance of many species. So he works hard to __18__ the animals' territory and protect their freedom.

I have a(n) __19__ interest in going to Africa to visit my cousin. There's nothing I'd rather do. In fact, I would go tomorrow because I am ready to have an unusual, __20__ adventure.

1. _____

2. _____

3. _____

4. _____

5. _____

6. _____

7. _____

8. _____

9. _____

10. _____

11. _____

12. _____

13. _____

14. _____

15. _____

16. _____

17. _____

18. _____

19. _____

20. _____

Challenge Writing

Save the Cat A cat is caught up high in a tree. It is your job to help the cat find its way to safety. Write an explanation of how you would rescue the cat from the tree. Use the Challenge Words below. Be sure to describe the situation and tell how you would go about solving the problem.

amiss	dissuade	futile	meager	prudent

Fun with Words

The clues and some of the letters from this puzzle are missing! Fill in the missing letters to complete each chapter word in the puzzle. Then write a clue for each word.

Across

1. _____

3. _____

6. _____

8. _____

10. _____

Down

2. _____

4. _____

5. _____

7. _____

9. _____

Review 1-3

Word Meanings Underline the word that is best defined by each phrase.

1. to stop oneself from doing something
   a. denounce   **b.** accelerate   **c.** despair   **d.** abstain

2. the state of being locked up
   a. captivity   **b.** annex   **c.** consequence   **d.** vocation

3. not allowed by law
   a. abominable   **b.** illicit   **c.** juvenile   **d.** judicious

4. long and dull
   a. elusive   **b.** mischievous   **c.** exotic   **d.** tedious

5. making good decisions
   a. figurative   **b.** vital   **c.** judicious   **d.** gruesome

6. to protect
   a. mismanage   **b.** commit   **c.** conserve   **d.** disguise

7. to make something known
   a. reveal   **b.** grovel   **c.** emigrate   **d.** denounce

8. the way something is done
   a. notation   **b.** procedure   **c.** vocation   **d.** constellation

9. violently cruel and wild
   a. juvenile   **b.** elusive   **c.** fierce   **d.** exotic

10. to make a charge against
    a. denounce   **b.** disguise   **c.** grovel   **d.** abstain

11. to go faster
    a. vibrate   **b.** accelerate   **c.** congregate   **d.** emigrate

12. horrible and scary
    a. elusive   **b.** tedious   **c.** figurative   **d.** gruesome

13. to describe in words or images
    a. smolder   **b.** depict   **c.** emigrate   **d.** sneer

14. the effect of a cause
    a. qualm   **b.** explosion   **c.** consequence   **d.** calorie

15. a fight or argument that lasts a long time
    a. terminal   **b.** notation   **c.** feud   **d.** tendon

16. to gather together as a group
    a. congregate   **b.** vibrate   **c.** commit   **d.** conserve

17. a person's line of work
   a. captivity   **b.** vocation   **c.** procedure   **d.** impact

18. absolutely necessary
   a. perishable   **b.** figurative   **c.** judicious   **d.** vital

19. to make a mess of
   a. mismanage   **b.** denounce   **c.** accelerate   **d.** abstain

20. a person running for office
   a. qualm   **b.** constellation   **c.** athlete   **d.** candidate

Sentence Completion
Choose the word from the box that best completes each of the following sentences. Write the word in the blank.

keen	emigrated	mischievous	annex	misfit
abominable	discontent	perishable	athlete	slogan

1. My brother is _____ —he loves to play tricks on people.

2. Have you visited the beautiful new _____ to the public library yet?

3. I try to keep a(n) _____ eye out for bargains on clothes.

4. After we moved, our dog seemed _____ until she got used to our new home.

5. I can't get the new _____ for Chippy's corn chips out of my head.

6. The food bank accepts items that are not _____ and do not have to be refrigerated.

7. The star _____ on our track team hurt her leg yesterday.

8. Our family _____ from France many years ago.

9. Cruelty to animals is _____ behavior for any person.

10. Darren felt like a(n) _____; he didn't like the popular band.

Fill in the Blanks
Underline the pair of words that best completes each sentence.

1. The fifty-year _____ between the families was caused by the Miller's _____ in the neighborhood ghost.

   a. disguise, tension   **c.** candidate, vocation

   b. feud, disbelief   **d.** grovel, notation

2. If you do not _____ from eating too much junk food, your stomach may feel the _____ .

   a. denounce, parody
   b. conserve, notation
   c. abstain, consequences
   d. reveal, tension

3. If you plan to _____ to being in the play, it is _____ that you rehearse your lines before practice.

   a. commit, vital
   b. depict, perishable
   c. mismanage, elusive
   d. emigrate, keen

4. After hearing the two _____ debate, I decided that Peters was far more _____ than Schmitt.

   a. juveniles, terminal
   b. candidates, keen
   c. calories, judicious
   d. slogans, mischievous

5. The novel's main character was a(n) _____ villain whose _____ deeds terrified and puzzled even the most skilled detectives.

   a. abominable, discontent
   b. exotic, juvenile
   c. savage, gruesome
   d. tedious, perishable

6. The surgical _____ is difficult and _____ .

   a. parody, perishable
   b. explosion, vital
   c. procedure, tedious
   d. captivity, terminal

7. For the pet show we _____ our puppy as the _____ snowman.

   a. denounced, illicit
   b. sneered, fierce
   c. emigrated, gruesome
   d. disguised, abominable

8. The judge's words had a(n) _____ on the _____ offenders.

   a. impact, juvenile
   b. explosion, fierce
   c. vocation, keen
   d. disbelief, mischievous

9. The _____ fans yelled out their _____ each time their idol scored a goal.

   a. savage's, parody
   b. athlete's, slogan
   c. constellation's, disbelief
   d. misfit's, implement

10. A(n) _____ person will never _____ a crime.

   a. illicit, vibrate
   b. savage, smolder
   c. judicious, commit
   d. enamel, mismanage

Classifying Words Sort the words in the box by writing each word to complete a phrase in the correct category.

accelerate	calories	congregated	consequence	constellation
disbelief	disguise	elusive	explosion	feud
fierce	illicit	juvenile	mischievous	mismanage
notation	perched	procedures	tension	vital

Words You Might Hear in Court

1. recognize the criminal's clever _____

2. commit an _____ act

3. the _____ of your actions

4. the jurors' _____ of the witness's story

5. a young _____ delinquent's only crime

Words You Might Hear at the Zoo

6. the _____ monkey's pranks

7. a _____ beast's frightening roar

8. a parrot _____ on a branch

9. a crowd _____ around an exhibit

10. the nervous _____ between the two male lions

Words You Might Hear in an Office

11. make a _____ in the file

12. follow all office _____

13. a long-standing _____ between the two departments

14. try not to _____ the project

15. figure out how to _____ the schedule

Words You Might Hear in a Science Laboratory

16. the boom of a chemical _____

17. looking at a _____ through a telescope

18. record _____ information in a log

19. analyzing the number of _____ in food

20. pin down an _____ idea

Word List

Read each word using the pronunciation key.

Basic Words

acute (ə kyo͞ot´)
appreciative (ə prē´ shə tiv)
cavity (kav´ ə tē)
consider (kən sid´ ər)
crystal (kris´ təl)
despise (di spīz´)
displace (dis plās´)
enforcement (in fôrs´ mənt)
flex (fleks)
gulf (gulf)
incomprehensible (in kom pri hen´ sə bəl)
legislate (lej´ is lāt)
nobility (nō bil´ i tē)
physical (fiz´ i kəl)
radiant (rā´ dē ənt)
scant (skant)
sheen (shēn)
solitary (sol´ i târ ē)
trifle (trī´ fəl)
volume (vol´ yo͞om)

Challenge Words

anonymous (ə nä nə məs)
dishearten (dis här´ tən)
eradicate (i ra´ də kāt)
insinuate (in sin´ yə wāt)
prescribe (pri skrīb´)

Word Study

Suffixes

The suffix *-hood* means *a condition of* or *a group of.*

adulthood (ə dult´ ho͝od) *(n.)* the condition of being an adult
childhood (chīld´ ho͝od) *(n.)* the condition of being a child
falsehood (fôls´ ho͝od) *(n.)* an untrue statement; a lie
livelihood (līv´ lē ho͝od) *(n.)* a means of living; a way to support
motherhood (mə´ thər ho͝od) *(n.)* the condition of being a mother
neighborhood (nā´ bər ho͝od) *(n.)* people living near one another

Be Careful!

Commonly Misspelled Words

everything	college	beautiful
elementary	always	awhile

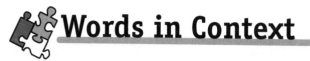# Words in Context

Read each sentence below to decipher the meaning of each boldface word. Use reasoning skills and the remainder of the sentence to help you. Write the meaning of the word on the line.

1. Your words are **incomprehensible** when you talk too quickly.

   _____

2. Wrestling takes great strength and is a very **physical** sport.

   _____

3. I **despise** cooked spinach, but I like raw spinach in a fresh salad.

   _____

4. I like to take **solitary** walks along the empty beach.

   _____

5. The officer's duty is to see to the **enforcement** of laws and arrest offenders.

   _____

6. Thank-you notes let others know that you are **appreciative** of their gifts.

   _____

7. I have a **cavity** in my tooth that the dentist needs to fill.

   _____

8. Take some time to **consider** each choice of dessert.

   _____

9. The duke and his cousin, the earl, come from a long family line of **nobility**.

   _____

10. The **radiant** glow from the fireplace warmed and cheered the room.

Word Meanings

Within each group, study the spelling, part(s) of speech, and meaning(s) of each word. Complete each sentence by writing the word on the line. Then read the sentence.

Basic Words

1. **acute** *(adj.)* 1. sharp; 2. keen, quick, intelligent

   Jason hit the ground, felt an _____ stab of pain, and knew his arm was broken.

2. **appreciative** *(adj.)* 1. having or showing gratitude; 2. recognizing the value of someone or something

   An actor's reward is the applause of an _____ audience.

3. **cavity** *(n.)* 1. a vacant space; 2. a hole

   Before cooking the turkey, fill the abdominal _____ with stuffing.

4. **consider** *(v.)* to think carefully about something before making a decision

   Think about the question and _____ your answer before speaking.

5. **crystal** *(n.)* a colorless, transparent rock or glass *(adj.)* 1. clear; 2. able to be seen through

   How long does it take to clean each _____ on the chandelier?

   We could see beautiful fish in the _____ clear water.

6. **despise** *(v.)* to dislike strongly

   I enjoy cooking, but I _____ washing all the dishes after the meal.

7. **displace** *(v.)* to replace or take the place of

   Will country-and-western music ever _____ rock and roll on this radio station?

8. **enforcement** *(n.)* a forcing to obey

   If drivers agree with the new speed limit, then _____ will be easy.

9. **flex** *(v.)* 1. to bend or move; 2. to move the muscles by contraction

   Come on now, _____ your arm so I can see your muscles.

10. **gulf** *(n.)* 1. a large section of an ocean or sea that has land around most of it; 2. a wide gap

Donald will follow the west coast of Florida as he sails the _____ .

11. **incomprehensible** *(adj.)* not understandable

The professor's speech was not only difficult to hear, it was _____ .

12. **legislate** *(v.)* to make or create laws

Congress ordered each state to _____ a slower highway speed limit.

13. **nobility** *(n.)* people who are of high rank, title, or birth

The palace and the royal yacht are only for the use of the British

_____ .

14. **physical** *(adj.)* of or relating to the body *(n.)* a medical examination by a physician

Let's get some _____ exercise by running a few football plays.

At my annual _____ , the doctor said I'm in great shape.

15. **radiant** *(adj.)* 1. bright; 2. shining; 3. beaming

The winner accepted her trophy with a _____ smile.

16. **scant** *(adj.)* barely enough in size or quantity

She held up the _____ piece of fabric and decided to make a skirt for her doll.

17. **sheen** *(n.)* 1. a brightness; 2. a glow

The winning dog's coat had a clean, healthy _____ .

18. **solitary** *(adj.)* 1. alone; 2. single; 3. isolated; 4. lonely

The park ranger enjoyed his _____ life in a remote mountain cabin.

19. **trifle** *(v.)* 1. to treat someone or something as unimportant; 2. to handle something idly

Do not _____ with airport security.

20. **volume** *(n.)* 1. the amount of space that something contains or fills; 2. a large amount of something; 3. the degree of loudness

Is the _____ of liquid in the tall glass the same as in the short glass?

Challenge Words

anonymous *(adj.)* not identified

I never did get the name of the _____ caller.

dishearten *(v.)* to make someone lose motivation or spirit

The bad weather may _____ the picnickers.

eradicate *(v.)* to remove completely, as if pulling up by the root

This weed killer should _____ the dandelions.

insinuate *(v.)* to communicate or suggest in an indirect way

He will _____ that you should hurry by pointing to his watch.

prescribe *(v.)* 1. to designate a plan or guide for; 2. to give a medical prescription

Doctor Sims will _____ some medicine to reduce your fever.

Synonyms

Synonyms are words that have the same or nearly the same meanings.

Part 1 Choose the word from the box that is the synonym for each group of words. Write the word on the line.

despise	sheen	scant	displace
solitary	crystal	legislate	appreciative

1. to enact, make laws, pass _____

2. scarce, insufficient, inadequate _____

3. a shine, polish, gloss _____

4. one, individual, lonesome _____

5. thankful, grateful, indebted to _____

6. to hate, scorn, condemn _____

7. transparent, see-through; a quartz _____

8. remove, dislodge, eject _____

Part 2 Replace the underlined word(s) with a word from the Basic Words list that means the same or almost the same thing. Write your answer on the line.

9. We flew over a <u>large body of water</u> on our way from Florida to Mexico.

_____

10. Our walkway was lined with <u>luminous</u> candlelight. _____

11. The veteran ballplayers off-handedly <u>fiddle</u> with their bats. _____

12. Each camper needs to have a <u>checkup</u> before leaving for camp.

_____

13. I can't read this because your handwriting is <u>unclear</u>. _____

14. The shah retained an air of <u>royalty</u>. _____

15. The jury is instructed to <u>weigh</u> the testimony of all witnesses carefully.

_____

Antonyms

Antonyms are words that have opposite or nearly opposite meanings.

Part 1 Choose the word from the box that is the antonym for each group of words. Write the word on the line.

acute	cavity	appreciative	solitary	sheen

1. giving no thanks, not obliged _____

2. dull, dim-witted, slow _____

3. a filled space, solid area　＿＿＿＿＿＿＿＿＿＿＿＿＿

4. a dimness　＿＿＿＿＿＿＿＿＿＿＿＿＿

5. accompanied, attended, surrounded　＿＿＿＿＿＿＿＿＿＿＿＿＿

Part 2 Replace the underlined word(s) with a word from the Basic Words list that means the opposite or almost the opposite thing. Write your answer on the line.

6. There is <u>plenty of</u> food in the pantry to feed this many people.

＿＿＿＿＿＿＿＿＿＿＿

7. The dining cars on the train are reserved for the <u>common people</u>.

＿＿＿＿＿＿＿＿＿＿＿

8. The directions for Paula's new computer were <u>easy to understand</u>.

＿＿＿＿＿＿＿＿＿＿＿

9. Our bulldogs <u>love</u> the cold weather. ＿＿＿＿＿＿＿＿＿＿＿

10. To improve your exercise session, <u>relax</u> your muscles frequently.

＿＿＿＿＿＿＿＿＿＿＿

Word Study/Suffixes

Choose the word from the box that best completes what each person said.

adulthood	livelihood	childhood
falsehood	neighborhood	motherhood

1. A young woman: Watching your child leave for their first day of school is a

   difficult part of ＿＿＿＿＿＿＿＿＿＿＿.

2. Senior citizen: I have been enjoying ＿＿＿＿＿＿＿＿＿＿＿ for a very long time.

3. Courtroom judge: I will not tolerate a single ＿＿＿＿＿＿＿＿＿＿＿ in this trial.

4. Community leader: We will work together to make this ＿＿＿＿＿＿＿＿＿＿＿ safe.

5. Teenager: I don't want bunkbeds anymore. I have left ＿＿＿＿＿＿＿＿＿＿＿ behind.

6. Firefighter: I rescue people and put out fires for my ＿＿＿＿＿＿＿＿＿＿＿.

Tell the Story

Choose the word from the Basic Words list that best completes each sentence. Write the word on the line. You may use the plural form of nouns and the past tense of verbs if necessary.

Last weekend I had a(n) __1__ attack of loneliness. It all started in __2__ education class where my big sister is a gym helper. At the other end of the gym, the boys' basketball team was practicing. It was fun to watch them shoot free throws and __3__ their muscles. So we paid __4__ attention when my sister Martha tried to get class started. Usually I __5__ Martha my best friend, but sometimes she takes being a gym helper a little too seriously. On Friday, she acted just like a law __6__ officer. She blew her whistle in an insulting way and shouted, "Okay, turn down the __7__. Line up NOW!"

My friends made a face, and I groaned out loud. "Martha acts like she thinks she's __8__." I said. "Someone should __9__ against bossy big sisters." The minute the words were out I was sorry. Of course I didn't mean it. Sometimes my behavior is __10__ even to me. Then I looked up, and there was my sister. From the look on her face it was __11__ clear that she had heard what I said.

At home after school, it felt like there was a(n) __12__ between Martha and me. It got worse when I was __13__ from our room by the girlfriend she invited to spend the weekend. I felt worse than the time I had a(n) __14__ in my tooth. After a(n) __15__ weekend, I was sadder than ever. I wanted to make up, but I didn't know what Martha would say. Finally I went to our room. Martha was brushing her hair. Her hair had a beautiful __16__, but her face looked sad. "I know you __17__ me," I began, "but I'm really sorry for what I said. I don't even know why I said it."

My sister's face broke into a(n) __18__ smile. "I'm sorry, too," she replied. "I didn't mean to __19__ with your feelings."

Sometimes people make mistakes, but real friends get over them. My sister and I are best friends again. And from now on we'll be more __20__ of each other.

1. _____
2. _____
3. _____
4. _____
5. _____
6. _____
7. _____
8. _____
9. _____
10. _____
11. _____
12. _____
13. _____
14. _____
15. _____
16. _____
17. _____
18. _____
19. _____
20. _____

Challenge Writing

After-School Bizarre Imagine you have planned an educational after-school program for all kids under twelve in your school, but something has gone haywire. The children have begun to take control. What can you do? Write about your experience. Use the Challenge Words below. Be sure to answer the questions *who, what, where, when, why,* and *how*.

anonymous	dishearten	eradicate	insinuate	prescribe

_____

_____

_____

_____

_____

_____

_____

_____

_____

_____

_____

_____

_____

_____

Fun with Words

Write the word from the Basic Words list that matches each definition. Write one letter of the word in each blank. Then use the numbered letters to answer the riddle.

1. water that has land around three sides

$\underline{}\ \underline{}\ \underline{}\ \underline{}$
$\quad\ \ _{1}\quad\ _{2}$

2. a forcing to obey

$\underline{}\ \underline{}\ \underline{}\ \underline{}\ \underline{}\ \underline{}\ \underline{}\ \underline{}\ \underline{}$
$\qquad\qquad\quad _{3}\qquad\qquad _{4}$

3. an examination by a doctor

$\underline{}\ \underline{}\ \underline{}\ \underline{}\ \underline{}\ \underline{}\ \underline{}$
$\quad\ \ _{5}$

4. barely enough in quantity

$\underline{}\ \underline{}\ \underline{}\ \underline{}\ \underline{}$
$\qquad\qquad _{6}$

5. bright and shining

$\underline{}\ \underline{}\ \underline{}\ \underline{}\ \underline{}\ \underline{}$
$\qquad\quad _{7}$

6. a colorless, transparent rock

$\underline{}\ \underline{}\ \underline{}\ \underline{}\ \underline{}\ \underline{}\ \underline{}$
$\ _{8}\qquad\qquad _{9}$

7. people of noble rank

$\underline{}\ \underline{}\ \underline{}\ \underline{}\ \underline{}\ \underline{}\ \underline{}$
$\quad\ _{10}\qquad\qquad\quad _{11}$

8. to take the place of

$\underline{}\ \underline{}\ \underline{}\ \underline{}\ \underline{}\ \underline{}\ \underline{}$
$\qquad\quad _{12}$

9. to handle something idly

$\underline{}\ \underline{}\ \underline{}\ \underline{}\ \underline{}\ \underline{}$
$\quad\ _{13}$

10. to bend or contract

$\underline{}\ \underline{}\ \underline{}\ \underline{}$
$\ _{14}$

Which president had the largest family?

$\underline{}\ \underline{}\ \underline{}\ \underline{}\ \underline{}\ \underline{}\quad \mathbf{W}\ \underline{}\ \underline{}\ \underline{}\ \underline{}\ \underline{}\ \underline{}\ \underline{}\ \underline{}\ \underline{}\ .$
$\ _{1}\ \ _{3}\ \ _{10}\ _{13}\ \ _{1}\ \ _{3}\qquad\ \ _{6}\ \ _{12}\ _{5}\ \ _{7}\ \ _{4}\ \ _{1}\ \ _{9}\ _{10}\ _{4}$

$\underline{}\ \underline{}\quad \mathbf{W}\ \underline{}\ \underline{}\ \underline{}\ \underline{}\ \underline{}\ \underline{}\ \underline{}\ \underline{}\ \underline{}\ \underline{}$
$\ _{5}\ \ _{3}\qquad\ \ _{6}\ _{12}\qquad _{9}\ \ _{5}\ \ _{3}\qquad\ _{14}\ _{6}\ \ _{9}\ \ _{5}\ \ _{3}\ _{13}$

$\underline{}\ \underline{}\quad \underline{}\ \underline{}\ \underline{}\quad \underline{}\ \underline{}\ \underline{}\ \underline{}\ \underline{}\ \underline{}\ \underline{}\ .$
$_{10}\ _{14}\quad _{10}\ \ _{2}\ _{13}\qquad\ _{8}\ _{10}\ \ _{2}\ \ _{4}\ \ _{9}\ _{13}\ _{11}$

Word List

Read each word using the pronunciation key.

Basic Words

absorb (ab sôrb´)
adhere (əd hēr´)
associate (*v.* ə sō´ shē āt) (*adj., n.* ə sō´ shē it)
celestial (sə les´ chəl)
contentment (kən tent´ mənt)
destiny (des´ tə nē)
disposable (dis pō´ zə bəl)
engrave (in grāv´)
frantic (fran´ tik)
gullible (gul´ ə bəl)
induce (in do͞os´)
leisure (lē´ zhər)
nomad (nō´ mad)
pedestal (ped´ is təl)
pigment (pig´ mənt)
radioactivity (rā dē ō ak tiv´ ə tē)
scholar (skol´ ər)
sparse (spärs)
triumph (trī´ əmf)
voluntary (vol´ ən târ ē)

Challenge Words

barren (bâr´ ən)
circumscribe (sər´ kəm skrīb)
inconsistent (in kən sis´ tənt)
lavish (lav´ ish)
plight (plīt)

Word Study

Root Words

The Latin root word *port* means *to carry.*

portable (pôrt´ ə bəl) (*adj.*) easily carried
portfolio (pôrt fō´ lē ō) (*n.*) a case for carrying papers
portage (pôr´ tij) (*v.*) to carry overland
transport (trans´ pôrt) (*n.*) a carrying from one place to another
export (ek spôrt´) (*v.*) to send out of one country
report (ri pôrt´) (*v.*) to give an account of something

Be Careful!

Commonly Misspelled Words

anniversary	famous	privilege
banana	doubt	occasion

# Words in Context

Read each sentence below to decipher the meaning of each boldface word.
Use reasoning skills and the remainder of the sentence to help you. Write the
meaning of the word on the line.

1. This sponge will **absorb** the water that I spilled.

_____

2. The Statue of Liberty stands on a large **pedestal.**

_____

3. My **gullible** cousin believed me when I said the moon is made of cheese.

_____

4. Quinn grinned in **triumph** when he came from behind and won the race.

_____

5. Mom used glue to **adhere** the sequins to my sister's costume.

_____

6. The **nomad** moved on, carrying everything he owned in a tapestry bag.

_____

7. Grandpa ran his hand over his head and said, "My hair is pretty **sparse** these days."

_____

8. Use **disposable** party cups so we won't have any glasses to wash later.

_____

9. The jeweler agreed to **engrave** Paige's name on her gold bracelet.

_____

10. Professor Garcia, a well-known **scholar** of anthropology, taught our class.

_____

Word Meanings

Within each group, study the spelling, part(s) of speech, and meaning(s) of each word. Complete each sentence by writing the word on the line. Then read the sentence.

Basic Words

1. **absorb** *(v.)* to soak up or take in

   Did you know that kitty litter will _____ an oil spill on the garage floor?

2. **adhere** *(v.)* to stick, cling, or hold tight

   Double-sided tape will _____ posters neatly to the wall.

3. **associate** *(v.)* 1. to join in thought; 2. to join as a friend or acquaintance *(adj.)* connected with one or more persons or things *(n.)* a friend, acquaintance, or colleague

   My cats _____ the sound of the can opener with their dinner.

   As a new member, Tim will begin as _____ director of the club.

   I would like to introduce my _____ from the office.

4. **celestial** *(adj.)* of or relating to the sky

   Do you ever look at the night sky and ponder the _____ bodies there?

5. **contentment** *(n.)* happiness or satisfaction

   A cup of cocoa gives me a feeling of _____.

6. **destiny** *(n.)* a person's fortune or fate

   It's a cowboy's _____ to ride the range for the rest of his life.

7. **disposable** *(adj.)* something made to be discarded after use

   _____ cups and plates are a good idea for the picnic.

8. **engrave** *(v.)* 1. to cut designs into a surface in an artistic way; 2. to carve

   "Please _____ 'To Sarah, with love' on this watch for my sweetie."

9. **frantic** *(adj.)* very excited with rage, fear, pain, or grief

   After a _____ search, we found the lost airline tickets.

10. **gullible** *(adj.)* 1. easily deceived; 2. unsuspecting

My _____ brother believed me when I said that our dog ate his homework.

11. **induce** *(v.)* 1. to influence or persuade; 2. to cause or bring about

Will counting imaginary sheep really _____ sleep?

12. **leisure** *(n.)* the time free from work in which one may rest or enjoy oneself *(adj.)* 1. not occupied; 2. free

After this hard winter, Sam deserved three days of _____ in Florida.

In her _____ time, Donna likes to play soccer.

13. **nomad** *(n.)* a member of a tribe that moves from one place to another in search of food and water

We met a desert _____ who invited us to travel with his people.

14. **pedestal** *(n.)* a base for a statue or a lamp

The gallery displayed Ed's sculpture on a green marble _____.

15. **pigment** *(n.)* a coloring matter in the cells of plants and animals

Pink eyes of an albino rabbit are the result of a lack of _____.

16. **radioactivity** *(n.)* the rays or tiny particles given off from atomic nuclei

Warning: Continued exposure to _____ can be harmful to your health.

17. **scholar** *(n.)* 1. a student; 2. a wise person; 3. a teacher

Sidney is a dedicated _____ who spends all of his time in the library.

18. **sparse** *(adj.)* 1. thinly scattered; 2. not thickly grown

The candidate was disappointed by the _____ crowd.

19. **triumph** *(v.)* to win success *(n.)* a victory

The team confidently expects to _____ over its final opponent.

Everyone celebrated the _____ of the championship volleyball team.

20. **voluntary** *(adj.)* 1. acting on one's own choice; 2. not forced or required

The town built the park with the help of _____ workers.

Challenge Words

barren *(adj.)* 1. not able to reproduce; 2. producing little

We can't grow crops in this _____ soil.

circumscribe *(v.)* to construct around or mark a boundary

To _____ a square, draw a circle that touches the four corners.

inconsistent *(adj.)* lacking consistency or logic in thought or action

Our _____ weather has been cold one day and warm the next.

lavish *(adj.)* producing in abundance

We have a _____ supply of apples because of perfect weather.

plight *(n.)* a difficult or unfortunate situation

A dog with a broken leg is in a sad _____ .

Synonyms

Synonyms are words that have the same or nearly the same meanings.

Part 1 Choose the word from the box that is the synonym for each group of words. Write the word on the line.

nomad	associate	adhere	sparse
triumph	scholar	pedestal	frantic

1. an educated person, professor   _____

2. to connect; a partner; joined   _____

3. to attach, cling, bond   _____

4. mad, wild, raging   _____

5. wanderer, migrant, traveler   _____

6. to succeed; conquer; accomplishment _____

7. thin, few, scanty _____

8. a stand, foundation, support _____

Part 2 Replace the underlined word(s) with a word from the Basic Words list that means the same or almost the same thing. Write your answer on the line.

9. Are you looking forward to a little <u>relaxation</u> time on the beach?

_____

10. The mother tried to <u>urge</u> her daughter to get dressed quickly. _____

11. Only <u>easily fooled</u> little kids could love this inept magician. _____

12. Some people look to a psychic to tell them their <u>future</u>. _____

13. After the hearty meal, a feeling of <u>comfort</u> settled over the diners.

_____

14. Lit by twinkling lights, the dance floor transformed into a <u>heavenly</u> paradise.

_____

15. The paper tablecloths are meant to be <u>thrown away</u>. _____

Antonyms

Antonyms are words that have opposite or nearly opposite meanings.

Part 1 Choose the word from the box that is the antonym for each group of words. Write the word on the line.

frantic	adhere	contentment
voluntary	celestial	disposable

1. of the earth _____

2. forced, controlled, compelled _____

3. to let go, separate, loosen _____

4. discomfort, misery, sadness _____

5. permanent, lasting, reusable   _____

6. peaceful, calm, tranquil   _____

Part 2 Replace the underlined word(s) with a word from the Basic Words list that means the opposite or almost the opposite thing. Write your answer on the line.

7. Try that coin trick on my cousin. He's <u>hard to fool</u>. _____

8. This new fabric is designed to <u>reflect</u> the rays of the sun. _____

9. The general pointed to the <u>abundant</u> medals on his uniform. _____

10. The final score told the whole story of the baseball team's <u>defeat</u>.

    _____

11. Will Saturday be a day of <u>work</u> for you? _____

Word Study/Root Words

Use the words in the box to complete the journal entries.

| portable | portfolio | portage |
| transport | export | report |

A Scientist's Journal

Day One: Off we go in our canoe on an important scientific mission. Our canoes are

our _____ into the deepest part of the rain forest. When the four of us

return, we will _____ our findings to the medical community.

Day Two: Bad luck. We had smooth sailing until the river became a waterfall and we

had to _____ our canoes and equipment overland for three miles.

Then our canoes capsized in rough water and we lost our _____

of scientific papers and a _____ tape recorder.

Day Three: Unbelievable success! We located the giant fungus we were looking for. Our

company plans to _____ this fuzzy, blue fungus to foreign countries. We

will be rich and famous for finding it. This fungus, we believe, is the cure for baldness.

Tell the Story

Choose the word from the Basic Words list that best completes each sentence. Write the word on the line. You may use the plural form of nouns and the past tense of verbs if necessary.

I had just settled down for two weeks of __1__ at a Caribbean resort and was filled with __2__ and a hearty seafood lunch. I was having fun imagining how I would quit the wandering ways of a news reporter, no longer live the life of a(n) __3__ , and __4__ to a daily schedule of only sitting on sun-kissed beaches. Suddenly, a(n) __5__ waiter came running up to my poolside chair. "Urgent telephone call," he said breathlessly.

It was my __6__ , Jake, at the newspaper. "Listen," he said. "There's a big story breaking. The editor wants you to take this assignment on a(n) __7__ basis, and I want to __8__ you to say yes. It's the story of the century!

"We know very little, and exact information is __9__ . Scientific experts and university __10__ are confirming that a huge meteor will hit the earth at exactly the spot where your vacation island is located.

"Grab a(n) __11__ camera at the souvenir store. We want pictures and a story about this great __12__ body hurtling down from the sky. It's your __13__ that your vacation has taken you so close to the action. This story is your chance for a journalism award. It's as if your name is already chosen and __14__ on a Pulitzer Prize."

I closed my eyes to imagine how my prize would look displayed on a(n) __15__ in the newspaper office.

Jake began to talk faster. "They think that if the meteor hits the ocean, the water will __16__ the shock. But waves will flood the island and drown everyone. If the meteor hits land, the __17__ will instantly kill every living thing. There's no hope for anyone, unless you do one thing."

"Yes, Jake," I said, getting excited. "Go on. Go on."

"Here's what you have to do to save yourself. Cover the __18__ of your skin with yellow paint and label yourself a(n) __19__ man."

Jake laughed in __20__ at his practical joke. "There's no meteor. I just called to wish you a restful vacation. See you in two weeks."

1. _____
2. _____
3. _____
4. _____
5. _____
6. _____
7. _____
8. _____
9. _____
10. _____
11. _____
12. _____
13. _____
14. _____
15. _____
16. _____
17. _____
18. _____
19. _____
20. _____

Challenge Writing

Disaster Reporter Bad weather has turned an area in your state into a disaster area. You are a newspaper reporter flying over the area in a helicopter. Your job is to describe the damage for readers. Write a news article about your observations. Use the Challenge Words below.

barren	circumscribe	inconsistent	lavish	plight

_____

_____

_____

_____

_____

_____

_____

_____

_____

_____

_____

_____

_____

_____

Fun with Words

Unscramble the letters to form words from the Basic Words list. Then draw a line to connect each unscrambled word with its definition.

Group 1

1. heedar   _____   a. to soak up

2. babors   _____   b. to bring about

3. unlovytar   _____   c. not forced

4. crantif   _____   d. to hold tight

5. cuined   _____   e. very excited with fear

Group 2

6. stealped   _____   f. to cut designs into

7. tencnemontt   _____   g. time away from work to rest

8. bleapossid   _____   h. satisfaction

9. surliee   _____   i. something thrown away after use

10. gaverne   _____   j. the base for a statue

Chapter 6

Word List

Read each word using the pronunciation key.

Basic Words

administration (əd min i strā´ shən)
bankrupt (baŋk´ rupt)
churn (chərn)
convert (kən vərt´)
destructive (di struk´ tiv)
disrespect (dis ri spekt´)
engulf (in gulf´)
friction (frik´ shən)
gully (gul´ ē)
inept (in ept´)
liberate (lib´ ə rāt)
negotiate (ni gō´ shē āt)
obligation (ob li gā´ shən)
pioneer (pi ə nēr´)
rage (rāj)
scoundrel (skoun´ drəl)
spectrum (spek´ trəm)
splendor (splen´ dər)
trudge (truj)
warrant (wôr´ ənt)

Challenge Words

braggart (brag´ ərt)
corrupt (kə rupt´)
embezzle (im bez´ əl)
hardy (här´ dē)
mar (mär)

Word Study

Prefixes

These prefixes tell about number.
The prefixes *uni-* and *mono-* mean *one*.
The prefix *bi-* means *two*.
The prefix *tri-* means *three*.

unicellular (yü´ nə sel´ yə lər) *(n.)* having one cell
monologue (mon´ ə lôg) *(n.)* a speech given by one person
monorail (mon´ ə rāl´) *(n.)* a single rail
bicycle (bī´ sik´əl) *(n.)* a vehicle with two wheels
bipolar (bī pō´ lər) *(adj.)* having two poles
triangle (trī´ aŋ gəl) *(n.)* a figure with three angles
tricolor (trī´ kul´ ər) *(adj.)* having three colors
tricycle (trī´ sə kəl) *(n.)* a vehicle with three wheels

Be Careful!

Commonly Misspelled Words

sometimes	baggage	civilization
icicle	biscuit	exhausted

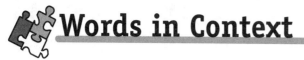# Words in Context

Read each sentence below to decipher the meaning of each boldface word. Use reasoning skills and the remainder of the sentence to help you. Write the meaning of the word on the line.

1. The **bankrupt** woman finally admitted that she could not pay her bills.

_____

2. Our school district's **administration** is headed by the superintendent.

_____

3. Mom and Dad's project is to **convert** the basement into a play area.

_____

4. Use the giant mixer to **churn** the eggs, milk, and sugar.

_____

5. The ball bearings in your skates reduce the **friction** of the moving parts.

_____

6. The hurricane might **rage** outside, but we will be calm and safe inside.

_____

7. If waves **engulf** the rowboat, be ready to bail out the water.

_____

8. The prism caught the sunlight and turned it to all the colors of the **spectrum.**

_____

9. I'm annoyed by people who show **disrespect** and talk throughout a movie.

_____

10. I was barely able to **trudge** up the last hill of our long hike.

_____

Word Meanings

Within each group, study the spelling, part(s) of speech, and meaning(s) of each word. Complete each sentence by writing the word on the line. Then read the sentence.

Basic Words

1. **administration** *(n.)* 1. the managing of a business, school, or office; 2. authoritative control over the business of others

   It is the decision of the school _____ to close another school.

2. **bankrupt** *(adj.)* unable to pay debts as declared by a court of law

   Unable to pay its debts, the _____ business closed its doors forever.

3. **churn** *(v.)* to stir or shake

   We'll take turns shaking this jar until we _____ the cream into butter.

4. **convert** *(v.)* to change from one form or use to another

   Remember to _____ your dollars into pesos at the airport.

5. **destructive** *(adj.)* 1. devastating; 2. destroying

   The _____ force of a tornado can flatten buildings.

6. **disrespect** *(n.)* 1. rudeness; 2. impoliteness

   _____ toward each other will not be tolerated.

7. **engulf** *(v.)* 1. to swallow up or enclose; 2. to overwhelm

   Stay in the harbor so that the waves do not _____ the boat.

8. **friction** *(n.)* a scraping of one thing against another

   Oil will reduce the _____ between the parts of the engine.

9. **gully** *(n.)* a trench made by heavy rains or running water

   The pickup truck made it through the _____ without being washed away.

10. **inept** *(adj.)* clumsy or awkward

    At first Liz was an _____ ice skater, but now she is graceful.

11. **liberate** *(v.)* to set free; 2. to deliver; 3. to release

The veterinarian decided to _____ the condor back into the wild.

12. **negotiate** *(v.)* 1. to come to an agreement; 2. to talk about

The owners and players will _____ the new contract.

13. **obligation** *(n.)* a duty under personal feeling or law

Once you sign the contract, you are under _____ to abide by it.

14. **pioneer** *(n.)* a person who settles in one territory, preparing and planning it for others *(v.)* to prepare or open up for others to follow

The _____ headed West, blazing a trail for those who would follow.

It takes great courage to _____ the last frontier — space.

15. **rage** *(v.)* to speak or act furiously *(n.)* anger, violent fury

It will not be a surprise if the protesters _____ against the city council.

The desperate townspeople flew into a _____ against the wicked king.

16. **scoundrel** *(n.)* a person without honor or good principles

Don't give your money to a _____ who is making false promises.

17. **spectrum** *(n.)* a band of color formed when light is dispersed through a prism

A rainbow has all the colors of the _____.

18. **splendor** *(n.)* 1. extreme brightness; 2. magnificence

The desert is a great place to enjoy the _____ of the sunset.

19. **trudge** *(v.)* to walk with effort

Please shovel the walk so that I do not have to _____ through the snow.

20. **warrant** *(n.)* 1. a reason that gives a right; 2. authority *(v.)* to justify or give a good reason for

The police had a _____ for the escaped convict's arrest.

Do nothing that will _____ punishment.

Challenge Words

braggart *(n.)* one who boasts loudly

The biggest _____ in school is always boasting about how many trophies she has.

corrupt *(v.)* to change from good to bad in values or actions *(adj.)* characterized by morally wrong behavior

We shouldn't _____ honest people by tempting them to break laws.

The _____ taxi driver charged his passengers twice the normal rate.

embezzle *(v.)* to use others' money or property for one's own personal gain

The bank teller didn't get away with her plan to _____ money by hiding it in her purse.

hardy *(adj.)* 1. capable of withstanding harsh conditions; 2. brave

This _____ husky pulls a dogsled through snow, ice, and bitter cold.

mar *(v.)* to injure, harm, or destroy

A sharp object may _____ the beautiful wooden tabletop.

Synonyms

Synonyms are words that have the same or nearly the same meanings.

Part 1 Choose the word from the box that is the synonym for each group of words. Write the word on the line.

inept	administration	friction	destructive
convert	gully	churn	engulf

1. graceless, blundering, not handy   _____

2. a ditch, ravine   _____

3. a rubbing of two things together   _____

4. to flood, submerge, swamp   _____

5. hurtful, harmful, causing injury _____

6. to transform, alter, rework _____

7. to shake up, mix, beat _____

8. management, supervision, guidance _____

Part 2 Replace the underlined word(s) with a word from the Basic Words list that means the same or almost the same thing. Write your answer on the line.

9. The falcon society promises to <u>free</u> all captured falcons. _____

10. You are under no <u>requirement</u> to buy any more CDs from the record club.

_____

11. Senator John Glenn, one of the first astronauts, was a space-age <u>pathfinder</u>.

_____

12. The skies turned dark and the winds blew in a <u>fury</u>. _____

13. Let's find the <u>rascal</u> who broke my window. _____

14. I watched the boy <u>plod</u> up the stairs carrying the heavy boxes. _____

15. Todd's helicopter flew over the <u>grandeur</u> of the Canadian Rocky Mountains.

_____

Antonyms

Antonyms are words that have opposite or nearly opposite meanings.

Part 1 Choose the word from the box that is the antonym for each group of words. Write the word on the line.

liberate	disrespect	convert	bankrupt	inept

1. to keep the same, maintain _____

2. courtesy, consideration, regard _____

3. wealthy, able to pay _____

4. competent, skillful, able _____

5. to confine, keep, restrict _____

Part 2 Replace the underlined word(s) with a word from the Basic Words list that means the opposite or almost the opposite thing. Write your answer on the line.

6. There was a <u>calmness</u> of the wind just before the hail fell. _____

7. As we drove through the village, we were amazed by its <u>drabness</u>.

   _____

8. I can tell how much you want to shop by the way you <u>glide</u> down the aisles of

   the store. _____

9. "Point out just one <u>honest, good person</u>," said the new sheriff. _____

10. The fishing is good where the waters <u>are calm</u>. _____

Word Study/Prefixes

Choose the word from the box that is associated with the following words. Write the word on the line.

unicellular	monologue	monorail	bicycle
bipolar	triangle	tricolor	tricycle

1. contrasting, extremes _____

2. red, white, and blue _____

3. a single track _____

4. handlebars, seat, pedals, two wheels _____

5. a wheel in front and two in back _____

6. amoeba, paramecium _____

7. a speech, a soliloquy _____

8. a musical instrument _____

Tell the Story

Choose the word from the Basic Words list that best completes each sentence. Write the word on the line. You may use the plural form of nouns and the past tense of verbs if necessary.

The newspaper reported that the zoo had run out of money and was __1__ . I went straight to the office of __2__ to talk with the zoo director. The director explained that last month's __3__ storm had been very damaging to the zoo. The heavy rainfall had caused a(n) __4__ to run through the zoo, destroying much of the landscaping. We had to __5__ through ankle-deep mud as the director took me on a tour of the damage. High winds __6__ that night and caused power outages because of the __7__ between tree limbs and power lines. An uprooted tree broke a window and __8__ many rare birds.

The men hired to repair the damage turned out to be __9__ and did not complete the job. Their __10__ for a public attraction affected thousands of people. The director explained that he was trying to __11__ with bill collectors in order to keep the zoo open. He said he has a(n) __12__ to the children of the city to keep the zoo open, but he didn't know if he could keep his commitment. I could see that the director needed help to __13__ his despair into a positive attitude. I could immediately see that the problem __14__ drastic and quick action.

I took photographs of the wreckage to the city newspaper to __15__ up support for an idea I had to help the zoo. I felt like such a brave __16__ . My idea spread quickly. On Saturday, hundreds of volunteers from all over the city __17__ the zoo, armed with ladders, paintbrushes, saws, and hammers. We supplied paint in all the colors of the __18__ . I'm a(n) __19__ painter, but I was nearly an expert by the end of the day. As the last volunteers left, I was amazed to find that the windows were mended and the mud was gone. The zoo had regained its beauty and __20__ .

1. _____
2. _____
3. _____
4. _____
5. _____
6. _____
7. _____
8. _____
9. _____
10. _____
11. _____
12. _____
13. _____
14. _____
15. _____
16. _____
17. _____
18. _____
19. _____
20. _____

Challenge Writing

Thief Caught You are a police officer. You have arrested a stranger for stealing money from a charity. Write a police report on this arrest. Use the Challenge Words below. Be sure to tell what the crime was and how it was committed.

braggart	corrupt	embezzle	hardy	mar

_____

_____

_____

_____

_____

_____

_____

_____

_____

_____

_____

_____

_____

_____

_____

Fun with Words

There are ten Basic Words hidden in this puzzle. The words may run across, up, down, forward, or backward. Find each word and circle it. Then use five of the words in sentences.

```
E T P B A N K E P T T I O N T R U M W
T D A A A D M I N I S T R A T I O N U
A E N N C H J L W A N E B S A G C O T
R R E K O F X M A I N E P T F U H I S
E O E R L U V M R Z Y X G L L L C T L
B A R U Q T U N R E L E L O K L O C K
I N G P P R P I A E R E L L T Y N I J
L R U T T W A R N S E L E R D I D R C
R X L C O N V R T R U D G E U O A F B
I W E N G L L G E T C E P S E D S T A
S P I O G A R N O I T A G I L B O M E
S S U A E I O Y F R C T N L I P B I L
```

1. _____

_____

2. _____

_____

3. _____

_____

4. _____

_____

5. _____

_____

Review 4-6

Word Meanings Underline the word that is best defined by each phrase.

1. feel scorn for
   a. displace   **b.** despise   **c.** engrave   **d.** liberate

2. shining brightly
   a. radiant   **b.** acute   **c.** scant   **d.** celestial

3. a lack of politeness
   a. contentment   **b.** destiny   **c.** disrespect   **d.** obligation

4. easily tricked
   a. physical   **b.** disposable   **c.** gullible   **d.** bankrupt

5. not thick or crowded
   a. sparse   **b.** voluntary   **c.** destructive   **d.** inept

6. an early settler
   a. scholar   **b.** nobility   **c.** nomad   **d.** pioneer

7. not with others
   a. leisure   **b.** solitary   **c.** physical   **d.** celestial

8. impossible to understand
   a. frantic   **b.** bankrupt   **c.** voluntary   **d.** incomprehensible

9. to take in
   a. churn   **b.** trifle   **c.** induce   **d.** absorb

10. a big victory
    a. crystal   **b.** triumph   **c.** pedestal   **d.** friction

11. to let go
    a. convert   **b.** trudge   **c.** liberate   **d.** flex

12. to talk over a problem
    a. displace   **b.** engulf   **c.** negotiate   **d.** associate

13. a feeling of great anger
    a. splendor   **b.** obligation   **c.** rage   **d.** trifle

14. grateful or thankful
    a. appreciative   **b.** destructive   **c.** sparse   **d.** incomprehensible

15. to remain attached
    a. rage   **b.** despise   **c.** warrant   **d.** adhere

16. wild with worry
    a. radiant   **b.** frantic   **c.** solitary   **d.** inept

17. the space something takes up
    a. gully   **b.** volume   **c.** leisure   **d.** enforcement

18. bungling or clumsy
    a. destructive   **b.** frantic   **c.** inept   **d.** gullible

19. shininess
    a. volume   **b.** destiny   **c.** radioactivity   **d.** sheen

20. the act of directing a business or office
    a. administration   **b.** spectrum   **c.** obligation   **d.** friction

Sentence Completion Choose the word from the box that best completes each of the following sentences. Write the word in the blank.

associate	converts	disposable	cavity	induce
consider	voluntary	engraved	legislate	scant

1. The deep _____ in the tree trunk was caused by a lightning strike.

2. Our team received the championship trophy with "First Place"

   _____ on it.

3. Don't _____ with people who spread gossip about others.

4. A mill _____ wheat grain into flour.

5. _____ what the world would be like if we all treated each other the way we want to be treated.

6. Some people say we live in a "throwaway" world because we use so many

   _____ products.

7. Such a(n) _____ amount of food will not feed all of these people.

8. We elect people to Congress to _____ for our country.

9. Participating in the project is _____ —we aren't trying to force people to take part.

10. Can't we _____ you to join the team?

Fill in the Blanks
Underline the pair of words that best completes each sentence.

1. The sheriff issued a(n) _____ for the _____ arrest.
   - **a.** enforcement, pioneer's
   - **b.** warrant, scoundrel's
   - **c.** pedestal, scholar's
   - **d.** obligation, associate's

2. The _____ of the view gave me a feeling of _____.
   - **a.** administration, rage
   - **b.** nobility, radioactivity
   - **c.** splendor, contentment
   - **d.** triumph, leisure

3. Mud and vapor shot out of the volcano's glowing _____ just before the mountain was _____ in boiling lava.
   - **a.** cavity, engulfed
   - **b.** pedestal, adhered
   - **c.** gully, liberated
   - **d.** crystal, absorbed

4. I enjoy the _____ life of a writer, but I also enjoy spending time with my _____.
   - **a.** destructive, nomads
   - **b.** incomprehensible, scoundrels
   - **c.** inept, administration
   - **d.** solitary, associates

5. Sheila thinks a career in law _____ will be her _____.
   - **a.** contentment, triumph
   - **b.** disrespect, obligation
   - **c.** enforcement, destiny
   - **d.** administration, leisure

6. The _____ will attempt to _____ a new contract.
   - **a.** pioneer, adhere
   - **b.** administration, negotiate
   - **c.** nomad, legislate
   - **d.** nobility, despise

7. We saw all the colors of the _____ in the _____ light show.
   - **a.** friction, gullible
   - **b.** spectrum, celestial
   - **c.** pigment, voluntary
   - **d.** splendor, bankrupt

8. Nothing can _____ me to break the promise I made to my _____.
   - **a.** induce, associate
   - **b.** displace, warrant
   - **c.** liberate, crystal
   - **d.** churn, pioneers

9. Too many _____ products may be _____ to our environment.
   - **a.** radiant, acute
   - **b.** voluntary, appreciative
   - **c.** sparse, physical
   - **d.** disposable, destructive

10. No subject is allowed to show _____ to a member of the _____.
    - **a.** obligation, pioneers
    - **b.** triumph, gully
    - **c.** disrespect, nobility
    - **d.** rage, cavity

Classifying Words
Sort the words in the box by writing each word to complete a phrase in the correct category.

administration	appreciative	associates	contentment	crystal
despise	disrespect	enforcement	gulf	gully
liberate	negotiate	nomad	obligations	physical
pioneers	rage	scholar	scoundrel's	sparse

Words You Might Use to Talk about People

1. give credit to your co-workers and _____

2. enjoy the traveling life of a _____

3. show the brilliance of a _____

4. admire the bravery of our country's first _____

5. put an end to the _____ bad deeds

Words You Might Use to Talk about Feelings

6. smile because you're _____ of your birthday gifts

7. _____ people who are mean and dishonest

8. give a sigh of _____ in front of the cozy fire

9. try to control your feelings of _____

10. showed _____ by the tone of her voice

Words You Might Use to Talk about Geography

11. see the terrain on a _____ map

12. go snorkeling in the _____ of Mexico

13. see forests become _____ as you get near the tundra

14. the sun shining down on a _____ clear lake

15. a _____ cut into the rock by running water

Words You Might Use to Talk about Government

16. working to _____ oppressed people everywhere

17. a new _____ in power after the election

18. the president's _____ to the citizens

19. ambassadors trying to _____ peace treaties

20. _____ of laws to keep citizens safe

Chapter 7

Word List

Read each word using the pronunciation key.

Basic Words

adventurous (ad ven´ chər əs)
beacon (bē´ kən)
civilize (siv´ i līz)
correspond (kôr i spond´)
detach (di tach´)
dissolve (di zolv´)
enlist (en list´)
gaseous (gas´ ē əs)
harbor (här´ bər)
inevitable (in ev´ i tə bəl)
literal (lit´ ər əl)
nonabrasive (non´ ə brā siv)
obscure (əb skyŏŏr´)
pedestrian (pə des´ trē ən)
pore (pôr)
react (rē akt´)
serene (sə rēn´)
sprawl (sprôl)
uphold (up hōld´)
weave (wēv)

Challenge Words

cater (kā´ tər)
dialogue (dī´ ə lôg)
expendable (ik spen´ də bəl)
magnitude (mag´ ni tōōd)
regime (rə zhēm´)

Word Study

Suffixes

The suffix *-ic* means *having the characteristic of* or *relating to.*

angelic (an jel´ ik) *(adj.)* like an angel
artistic (är tis´ tik) *(adj.)* of art or artists
athletic (ath let´ ik) *(adj.)* like an athlete
dramatic (drə mat´ ik) *(adj.)* having to do with plays
historic (hi stôr´ ik) *(adj.)* important in history
photographic (fō tə graf´ ik) *(adj.)* relating to photography

Be Careful!

Commonly Misspelled Words

restaurant	Wednesday	congratulations
exercise	quotient	pumpkin

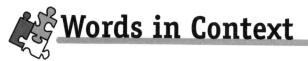 **Words in Context**

Read each sentence below to decipher the meaning of each boldface word.
Use reasoning skills and the remainder of the sentence to help you. Write the
meaning of the word on the line.

1. Faced with the **inevitable** sinking of their ship, the sailors swam for shore.

   _____

2. Before you fix a broken caboose, **detach** it from the rest of the train.

   _____

3. High waves prevented the ships from leaving the safe **harbor.**

   _____

4. When 6-foot Ryan **sprawled** on the couch, no one else could sit down.

   _____

5. This **nonabrasive** cleanser gently cleans the kitchen counter.

   _____

6. Every week I **correspond** with my pen pal in Saudi Arabia.

   _____

7. Jessica will **uphold** family tradition by becoming a dentist like her mother.

   _____

8. At night, tall buildings are illuminated with a red **beacon** so low-flying aircraft can
   see them.

   _____

9. Tanner had no time to **react** as the tennis ball flew past him.

   _____

10. The town's **serene** atmosphere changed when the circus arrived.

   _____

Word Meanings

Within each group, study the spelling, part(s) of speech, and meaning(s) of each word. Complete each sentence by writing the word on the line. Then read the sentence.

Basic Words

1. **adventurous** *(adj.)* 1. fond of risk; 2. full of hazard or danger

    Our _____ puppy returned from the woods smelling like a skunk.

2. **beacon** *(n.)* a light used as a signal to warn or guide

    The lighthouse _____ guided the ship towards the harbor.

3. **civilize** *(v.)* to advance from a primitive way of life

    The explorers' mission was to _____ the life of primitive people.

4. **correspond** *(v.)* 1. to agree; 2. to exchange letters with another

    I _____ with a girl in Japan and I eagerly await her letters.

5. **detach** *(v.)* 1. to remove or unfasten; 2. to separate

    Would you _____ the house key from your key chain and give it to me?

6. **dissolve** *(v.)* 1. to become liquid; 2. to end

    The soap powder will _____ in warm water.

7. **enlist** *(v.)* 1. to get help; 2. to secure support and aid; 3. to voluntarily go into the armed forces or another group

    If math is puzzling you, then please _____ a tutor to help you study.

8. **gaseous** *(adj.)* in a form that has neither a definite shape nor volume

    After the volcano erupted, all that remained was a _____ cloud of vapor.

9. **harbor** *(n.)* a sheltered place for ships *(v.)* to provide shelter to

    Fishing is allowed only off the pier in the _____.

    The veterinarian offered to _____ the orphaned fox pups.

10. **inevitable** *(adj.)* 1. something that is sure or certain; 2. unavoidable

    The pregame party will begin the celebration of the _____ victory.

11. **literal** *(adj.)* 1. word for word; 2. exact; 3. precise

    A _____ translation is not as beautiful as reading the poem in French.

12. **nonabrasive** *(adj.)* not causing irritation

    Use a _____ cleanser on your glasses.

13. **obscure** *(adj.)* 1. unknown; 2. unclear *(v.)* 1. to hide from view; 2. to dim or darken

    Marcy gives such _____ directions that I can never find her house.

    Overgrown shrubbery and vines _____ the secret door.

14. **pedestrian** *(n.)* 1. one who walks; 2. a person who travels by foot

    The _____ waited for traffic to pass before crossing the street.

15. **pore** *(n.)* a very tiny opening *(v.)* to gaze at or examine long and steadily

    He could feel the healing cream seep into each _____ of his skin.

    Just before a big test, Vicki and Rob _____ over their class notes.

16. **react** *(v.)* to respond to something or someone

    When you hear the alarm, I want each of you to _____ quickly.

17. **serene** *(adj.)* 1. peaceful; 2. calm; 3. quiet

    A summer morning's sunrise puts Annie in a _____ mood.

18. **sprawl** *(v.)* to spread out in an irregular or awkward manner

    Since there are no chairs left, you can _____ on the floor.

19. **uphold** *(v.)* 1. to support; 2. to not let down

    The police will take extra care this weekend to _____ the speed laws.

20. **weave** *(v.)* 1. to go by twisting and turning; 2. to interlace threads to make a cloth

    The New Year's dragon will _____ through the streets of China.

Challenge Words

cater *(v.)* to supply or provide what is required

We have all the food we need to _____ your party for you.

dialogue *(n.)* 1. an exchange of words between persons; 2. a conversation

The referee and the coach had an angry _____ about the final score.

expendable *(adj.)* normally used and easily replaced

The teacher considers pencils and paper to be _____ supplies.

magnitude *(n.)* the importance or quality of something

This prize-winning entry is a poem of the highest _____ .

regime *(n.)* 1. regular pattern or process of action; 2. a form of government

The president's new _____ begins when he takes the oath of office.

Synonyms

Synonyms are words that have the same or nearly the same meanings.

Part 1 Choose the word from the box that is the synonym for each group of words. Write the word on the line.

enlist	pore	sprawl	uphold
inevitable	correspond	harbor	obscure

1. to gain assistance _____

2. to lounge, extend, slouch _____

3. vague, uncertain; to conceal _____

4. inescapable, sure to happen _____

5. to match, fit; to communicate _____

6. a port, wharf; to shield, protect _____

7. to maintain, sustain, defend _____

8. a tiny hole; to inspect, survey _____

Part 2 Replace the underlined word(s) with a word from the Basic Words list that means the same or almost the same thing. Write your answer on the line.

9. The shoulder straps <u>disconnect</u> on some backpacks. _____

10. The <u>undisturbed</u> beauty of the Texas hills can be seen best from horseback.

_____

11. Who changes the light bulb in the <u>signal</u> on top of the Sears Tower?

_____

12. My favorite candy claims to <u>melt</u> in my mouth, not in my hand.

_____

13. The newspaper claimed to have a <u>real</u> account by an eyewitness.

_____

14. Steven undertook a <u>bold</u> journey in a hot air balloon. _____

15. My doctor has a <u>soothing</u> voice. _____

Antonyms

Antonyms are words that have opposite or nearly opposite meanings.

Part 1 Choose the word from the box that is the antonym for each group of words. Write the word on the line.

weave	obscure	detach	serene	enlist

1. troubled, rough, excited _____

2. to attach, bind, connect _____

3. to make a beeline, go straight as an arrow _____

4. obvious, well-known; to expose, show _____

5. to reject, refuse, not ask for _____

Part 2 Replace the underlined word(s) with a word from the Basic Words list that means the opposite or almost the opposite thing. Write your answer on the line.

6. It's a <u>routine</u> climb to the top of Mount Everest for the veteran climbers.

_____

7. The debaters changed their opinions so that they would <u>disagree</u>.

_____

8. The author revealed the <u>figurative</u> meaning of her story. _____

9. With your grades, it is <u>uncertain</u> that you will be on the honor roll.

_____

10. Rosie's <u>irritating</u> personality is unforgettable. _____

Word Study/Suffixes

Choose the word from the box that best completes each phrase. Write your answer on the line.

historic	athletic	photographic
artistic	angelic	dramatic

1. A child who is very kind and sweet-natured: a(n) _____ child

2. An ability to play and excel at sports: a(n) _____ ability

3. A community where many writers and painters live: a(n) _____ community

4. A play that has a serious theme: a(n) _____ play

5. A place that helps us understand the past: a(n) _____ place

6. A process that develops pictures made by a camera: a(n) _____ process

Tell the Story

Choose the word from the Basic Words list that best completes each sentence. Write the word on the line. You may use the plural form of nouns and the past tense of verbs if necessary.

Marcus and Felix, two __1__ boys who loved excitement, decided to spend Saturday exploring the ships and shoreline of the city __2__ . They __3__ the aid of their big sister, Debbie. "Of course I'll take you," Debbie said. "Someone has to __4__ you two rascals and be sure you behave."

So off they went on foot, three __5__ who were quite certain that they would find the __6__ adventure. At the pier, Debbie __7__ the pack from her waist and pulled out a guidebook. While she __8__ over the book, the boys stood on the pier watching jet skis __9__ around the buoys. "Yuk," they said as a(n) __10__ cloud erupted from the smoke stack of an old steamship. They could also see people at the old lighthouse that once served as a(n) __11__ to incoming ships. The boys looked at each other and at the same time their thoughts __12__ : The lighthouse was open! They expected Debbie to balk and __13__ with a firm "No way," but Debbie, determined to __14__ her role as older sister, led the way.

Some of the boys' energy __15__ as they trudged up and up the circular stairway. As they huffed and puffed, they vaguely remembered some __16__ purpose they had for climbing to the top, but it no longer seemed important. But when they finally reached the top, the view of the buildings and streets __17__ below them to the west and the gentle roll of the calm ocean to the east cast a(n) __18__ feeling over all of them.

They learned that the shiny brass lantern housing the great light was polished each day with a(n) __19__ cleanser to remove corrosive salt spray. And they learned that the __20__ translation of the Latin words on the side of the lantern was "I light the way."

1. _____

2. _____

3. _____

4. _____

5. _____

6. _____

7. _____

8. _____

9. _____

10. _____

11. _____

12. _____

13. _____

14. _____

15. _____

16. _____

17. _____

18. _____

19. _____

20. _____

Challenge Writing

A Strange Land Imagine that you are making a movie about a strange, faraway place. Write a journal entry about your adventures using the Challenge Words below. Be sure to describe the place, and the people, and their strange customs.

cater	dialogue	expendable	magnitude	regime

_____

_____

_____

_____

_____

_____

_____

_____

_____

_____

_____

_____

_____

_____

_____

_____

_____

Fun with Words

The nation of Varon has just discovered a group of rare land whales living on a nearby island. The whales would like to move to the mainland, but they're scared of the ocean and refuse to swim over. Varon's leaders have decided to build a bridge from the mainland to the whales' island.

You have been called in to build the bridge with your chapter vocabulary words. Read the definitions below, and place the correct vocabulary words in the blank bridge spaces provided. When you have supplied all the definitions, the land whales will be able to cross safely.

Across

4. to change to a liquid
5. to respond
8. doesn't irritate
10. precise

Down

1. having no defined size or shape
2. to have the same opinion
3. a signal light
6. to educate and advance
7. to give shelter
9. to spread out

Chapter 8

Word List

Read each word using the pronunciation key.

Basic Words

advisable (ad vī´ zə bəl)
besiege (bi sēj´)
clarity (klâr´ i tē)
corridor (kôr´ i dər)
detect (di tekt´)
distort (di stôrt´)
enrage (en rāj´)
gasp (gasp)
impede (im pēd´)
initiative (i nish´ ə tiv)
mangle (maŋ´ gəl)
observation (ob zər vā´ shən)
persuasion (pər swā´ zhən)
posterity (pä stâr´ ə tē)
rebel (*n., adj.* reb´ əl)(*v.,* ri bel´)
shaft (shaft)
stamina (stam´ ə nə)
timid (ti´ mid)
urban (ər´ bən)
whisk (hwisk)

Challenge Words

clamor (klam´ ər)
denote (di nōt´)
dynasty (dī´ nə stē)
paradox (pâr´ ə doks)
utmost (ut´ mōst)

Word Study

Prefixes

The prefix *post-* means *after* or *later.*

postdate (pōst dāt´) *(v.)* to give a later date
postgraduate (pōst gra´ jə wət) *(adj.)* continuing school after high school or college
postpone (pōst pōn´) *(v.)* to put off until later
postscript (pōst´ skript) *(n.)* a message written after the writer's name has been signed to a piece of correspondence
posttest (pōst´ test) *(n.)* a test given after something is taught
postwar (pōst wôr´) *(adj.)* after a war

Be Careful!

Commonly Misspelled Words

vacation	cousin	musician
brought	enough	league

# Words in Context

Read each sentence below to decipher the meaning of each boldface word. Use reasoning skills and the remainder of the sentence to help you. Write the meaning of the word on the line.

1. Yuki laughs when the warped funhouse mirrors **distort** her reflection.

_____

2. Joe's efforts to **impede** the growth of weeds in his yard were unsuccessful.

_____

3. Our cat would **detect** a visitor even before the doorbell rang.

_____

4. It takes **initiative** for Ken to wake up at 4:30 A.M. to practice gymnastics.

_____

5. My brothers **enrage** me when they tease about my boyfriend.

_____

6. We tried to **whisk** away all signs of the food fight before my parents returned.

_____

7. The runner's incredible **stamina** allowed her to complete the three-day race.

_____

8. The moving van rolled over Jeff's bike and **mangled** it.

_____

9. The diver stayed underwater too long and had to **gasp** for air.

_____

10. Random guessing is not an **advisable** course of action for a final exam.

_____

Word Meanings

Within each group, study the spelling, part(s) of speech, and meaning(s) of each word. Complete each sentence by writing the word on the line. Then read the sentence.

Basic Words

1. **advisable** *(adj.)* 1. sensible; 2. wise; 3. proper

   The school board hopes to reach an _____ decision.

2. **besiege** *(v.)* to crowd around someone or something in an effort to capture

   "Onward," cried the knight. "_____ the fortress."

3. **clarity** *(n.)* the condition of being clear and understandable

   He spoke with great _____ and for the first time I understood fractions.

4. **corridor** *(n.)* a long passage or hallway that leads into open rooms

   Go up the stairs, walk down the _____, and open the back door.

5. **detect** *(v.)* 1. to discover; 2. to learn

   Turn down the radio; I think I _____ a strange noise outside.

6. **distort** *(v.)* 1. to change shape by pushing, pulling, or twisting; 2. to twist something from its true meaning

   This mask is great because I can _____ the shape of the nose.

7. **enrage** *(v.)* 1. to fill with anger; 2. to make mad

   Do not _____ the caged lion by blowing that whistle.

8. **gasp** *(v.)* to try to get one's breath

   I had to _____ for air after running the marathon.

9. **impede** *(v.)* 1. to interfere with; 2. to obstruct

   Today's heavy rainfall will _____ the runners' progress.

10. **initiative** *(n.)* an active or energetic part in beginning any undertaking

    A great quarterback takes the _____ when his team is behind.

11. **mangle** *(v.)* to cut or tear with great force

    Set the washer on delicate or it might _____ your silk blouse.

12. **observation** (n.) 1. the act of watching and noting; 2. a remark or comment

The farmer's _____ that good weather was coming was true.

13. **persuasion** (n.) the process of convincing someone to do or believe something

To get a raise in her allowance, Hannah needs to use gentle _____.

14. **posterity** (n.) 1. future generations; 2. all of one's offspring

For the sake of _____, do not cut down the oak trees.

15. **rebel** (n.) a person who defies or fights against someone of authority instead of obeying (adj.) resisting law or authority (v.) 1. to defy or fight against the law of authority; 2. to feel a great dislike or opposition of someone or something

After Steve dyed his hair green, his friends called him a _____.

Many villagers were killed in the _____ uprising.

Do you expect any students to _____ against the new rules?

16. **shaft** (n.) a long, narrow passage that is similar to a well

The miners stood at the top of the _____ and discussed their next move.

17. **stamina** (n.) endurance or strength

Long distance swimmers require a great deal of ability and _____.

18. **timid** (adj.) lacking courage

Our _____ cat is frightened by loud noises.

19. **urban** (adj.) of or relating to cities or towns

Mrs. Green chose to live in an _____ community instead of on a farm.

20. **whisk** (n.) 1. a rapid sweep; 2. a light, rapid movement (v.) to move rapidly

With a _____ of her jeweled hand, the princess dismissed her servants.

Let's _____ the broom across the floor and clean this place quickly.

Challenge Words

clamor *(n.)* loud noise *(v.)* to make a loud noise

The lawn mower made such a _____ that it woke me up.

My baby brothers _____ for food if they're not fed on time.

denote *(v.)* 1. to stand for or signify; 2. to designate

We _____ poison with a drawing of a skull and crossbones.

dynasty *(n.)* a series of rulers from the same family or group

A _____ of kings has ruled the country for a thousand years.

paradox *(n.)* something or someone that has contradictory qualities

A friendly enemy is a real _____ .

utmost *(adj.)* the highest attainable point

I will need your _____ cooperation to finish this job on time.

Synonyms

Synonyms are words that have the same or nearly the same meanings.

Part 1 Choose the word from the box that is the synonym for each group of words. Write the word on the line.

impede	rebel	enrage	besiege	clarity	detect	initiative

1. a revolutionary; to rise up; defiant _____

2. to aggravate, inflame, madden _____

3. to block, stop, deter _____

4. to storm, try to capture _____

5. a first step, an introductory act _____

6. to observe, notice, perceive _____

7. plainness, simplicity _____

Part 2 Replace the underlined word(s) with a word from the Basic Words list that means the same or almost the same thing. Write your answer on the line.

8. After years of <u>viewing</u>, the astronomer discovered a new star. _____

9. The firefighter had to <u>gulp</u> for air when he came out of the smoke-filled building.

_____

10. The video game instructions say it is a <u>recommended</u> procedure to start at

Level One. _____

11. A lawn mower that is working poorly will <u>damage</u> the grass instead of cut it.

_____

12. Brad wished he had the <u>energy</u> to swim across the lake. _____

13. Joy wanted someone to <u>speed</u> her away to a sunny beach. _____

14. Every door in the hotel's long <u>hall</u> looked alike. _____

15. The heat from the radiator will <u>deform</u> any nearby plastic toys. _____

Antonyms

Antonyms are words that have opposite or nearly opposite meanings.

Part 1 Choose the word from the box that is the antonym for each group of words. Write the word on the line.

advisable	stamina	distort	impede	whisk

1. a weakness, lack of power _____

2. to crawl, drag; a slow motion _____

3. to keep in proper form _____

4. not recommended, improper _____

5. to promote, open the way for _____

Part 2 Replace the underlined word(s) with a word from the Basic Words list that means the opposite or almost the opposite thing. Write your answer on the line.

6. The groomer wondered why quiet music seemed to <u>calm</u> the horses.

_____

7. <u>Rural</u> houses come in all different shapes and sizes. _____

8. When King George's laws were read aloud, the colonists decided to <u>submit</u>.

_____

9. The new schedule resulted in greater <u>confusion</u> in the operation of the school.

_____

10. The anthropologist told us that the people she studied had great respect for

their <u>ancestors</u>. _____

Word Study/Prefixes

Choose the word from the box that best completes each pair of sentences. Write the word in the blank. You may use the past tense of verbs if necessary.

| postgraduate | postscript | postwar |
| posttest | postpone | postdate |

1. There were lots of jobs and money after World War II. It was _____ prosperity.

2. After high school she decided to attend college. She wanted to do

_____ work in the field of medicine.

3. Eric wrote a check today, but he put tomorrow's date on it. He _____ the check.

4. Cathy wrote a note at the end of her letter. The _____ said, "PS I love you."

5. We can't go to the theater tonight because of the weather. We will need to

_____ our plans.

6. Michael is able to skip the sixth grade math book. He performed so well on the fifth

grade _____ that he has advanced to the seventh grade math book.

Tell the Story

Choose the word from the Basic Words list that best completes each sentence. Write the word on the line. You may use the plural form of nouns and the past tense of verbs if necessary.

Doors __1__ open and closed with a swoosh as Jason angrily walked down the long __2__ of the starship. He had just learned that a report to the command center had __3__ facts about his leadership. The report said

- that he had used poor judgment in befriending a remote alien race
- that __4__ action would have been to __5__ the colony and destroy its populated __6__ areas
- that he had ignored all logic and the only __7__ he had listened to was the persuasion of his own cowardice.

The report __8__ Jason, but that did not prevent him from thinking with __9__ .

Just two light-years ago, Jason was congratulated for taking the __10__ to visit the government of a formerly hostile race. His careful __11__ of the situation later helped to make them an ally.

Now, someone was trying to __12__ his crew's mission and destroy and __13__ his good reputation with lies. He had heard rumors that his second lieutenant, Qwerty, wanted to be starship captain. Maybe Qwerty wanted to be captain at all costs.

Jason arrived at Qwerty's cabin. It seemed empty, but his telecommunicator __14__ a faint noise from the open vent of a pressurizing shaft. "Qwerty, I know you're here, and I know I have the __15__ to survive any attack you can make on me," Jason said.

He heard someone __16__ for breath. Then a small, __17__ voice from the __18__ said, "How did you know it was me?"

"The postscript on the bottom of the report was in your handwriting," Jason said. "Qwerty, you are dismissed from this crew. There is no room on this starship for a(n) __19__ who causes trouble only for his own benefit. The work we do is for all __20__ ."

1. _____

2. _____

3. _____

4. _____

5. _____

6. _____

7. _____

8. _____

9. _____

10. _____

11. _____

12. _____

13. _____

14. _____

15. _____

16. _____

17. _____

18. _____

19. _____

20. _____

Challenge Writing

Time Traveler Imagine that you traveled back in time. The ruler of an ancient civilization asked you to solve a serious problem affecting a great number of people. Using the Challenge Words below, write a letter to a friend telling what happened. Be sure to describe the problem and how you helped to solve it.

clamor	denote	dynasty	paradox	utmost

_____

_____

_____

_____

_____

_____

_____

_____

_____

_____

_____

_____

_____

Fun with Words

Hidden among the letters below are eleven of your chapter vocabulary words. They are written backward, forward, up, down, and diagonally. Your task is to find all the words and circle them. Hint: To know which words to look for, fill in the correct words next to the clues.

Clues

1. resisting law or authority _____

2. to tear with great force _____

3. to find out _____

4. a long, thin tunnel _____

5. not brave _____

6. to try to get one's breath _____

7. of or relating to cities _____

8. a long hallway _____

9. to obstruct _____

10. the state of being clear _____

11. to make mad _____

```
T V E J U N R S Z W O I E E R S
M F L H J Y F Z E U Y D M N E C
N O G I E F E D E T X S E B B E
T O N H W J G L I G E T D Y E U
I D A U B R S R E I A B U U L A
M B M W S K A C D W I R H K S B
I U E Q U L V B O K B E N T U T
D M F H C H U Y D A S N M E G C
Y R T U K O J I N C T X O G C E
M S J F I E R F A S B Y V O T T
W Y U U A G L R S N I M P E D E
E K K W O H O T I O D G R S E D
G U I D N S S R E D V R E C E O
C P S A G N Y U V L O G R O P T
I B G E M U I F E A V R G E A T
T S J F E A B H I U N R O S Y V
```

Chapter 9

Word List

Read each word using the pronunciation key.

Basic Words

aerial (âr´ ē əl)
blight (blīt)
classification (klas ə fə kā´ shən)
council (koun´ səl)
debate (di bāt´)
deter (di tər´)
division (di vizh´ ən)
entangle (en taŋ´ gəl)
generate (jen´ ə rāt)
horde (hôrd)
inquire (in kwīr´)
manipulate (mə nip´ yə lāt)
obstacle (ob´ stə kəl)
perspective (pər spek´ tiv)
precaution (pri kô´ shən)
recuperate (ri kōō´ pə rāt)
shed (shed)
stir (stər)
valiant (val´ yənt)
wholesome (hōl´ səm)

Challenge Words

countenance (*n., v.* koun´ tə nəns)
foremost (fôr´ mōst)
nostalgia (nə stal´ jə)
orthodox (ôr´ thə doks)
vigilant (vij´ ə lənt)

Word Study

Analogies

Analogies show relationships between pairs of words. Study the relationships between the pairs of words in the analogies below.

give is to **receive** as **save** is to **spend**

chick is to **hen** as **kitten** is to **cat**

five is to **ten** as **eight** is to **sixteen**

Be Careful!

Commonly Misspelled Words

patience	journal	discussion
necessary	lightning	watch

 # Words in Context

Read each sentence below to decipher the meaning of each boldface word. Use reasoning skills and the remainder of the sentence to help you. Write the meaning of the word on the line.

1. The **horde** of happy fans rushed the field and tore down the goalposts.

_____

2. The detectives hoped new clues would **shed** light on the baffling crime.

_____

3. Before Tommy returns to school, he will **recuperate** from the flu at home.

_____

4. A spider can **entangle** several small bugs in its web.

_____

5. The **stir** caused by the president's arrival did not calm down for hours.

_____

6. The candidates continued to **debate** the issue of taxes until time ran out.

_____

7. Clever Diana is able to **manipulate** her brother into washing the dog for her.

_____

8. Our town's annual Kite Day provides a spectacular **aerial** display.

_____

9. John and Joan negotiated an equal **division** of the weekend chores.

_____

10. Our **perspective** from the mountaintop made the town below look small.

_____

Word Meanings

Within each group, study the spelling, part(s) of speech, and meaning(s) of each word. Complete each sentence by writing the word on the line. Then read the sentence.

Basic Words

1. **aerial** *(adj.)* in or relating to the air

   The _____ display of the biplanes is my favorite part of the air show.

2. **blight** *(n.)* something that destroys or ruins

   The corn _____ is causing the farmers to have a poor crop this year.

3. **classification** *(n.)* arrangement into groups according to some system

   The _____ of books is determined by the Dewey decimal system.

4. **council** *(n.)* a gathering of people called together to give guidance and settle disagreements

   Neighborhood issues are discussed at meetings of the city _____.

5. **debate** *(n.)* a discussion about a question or topic *(v.)* 1. to discuss; 2. to talk about

   Ms. Lee's speech class held a _____ to discuss year-round classes.

   The senior citizens _____ issues of the day at the coffee shop.

6. **deter** *(v.)* to keep something from happening; 2. to prevent

   Snowfall is delaying airplanes and will _____ our arrival until tomorrow.

7. **division** *(n.)* 1. a separation; 2. sharing some with each

   If we assign a _____ of tasks, we will get the job done quicker.

8. **entangle** *(v.)* 1. to wrap up or catch; 2. to interweave

   Howie learned to toss the fishing net so he wouldn't _____ himself.

9. **generate** *(v.)* to create, produce, or make

   The circus manager is expecting the parade to _____ excitement.

10. **horde** *(n.)* 1. a swarm of people; 2. a crowd

    Times Square filled up with a _____ of New Year's revelers.

11. **inquire** *(v.)* to find out by asking questions

Let's _____ about the starting times for the new movie.

12. **manipulate** *(v.)* to control by clever use of unfair influence

The movie director can _____ emotions with sad music.

13. **obstacle** *(n.)* something that stands in the way of progress

The fallen tree was one _____ in Goldilocks's path.

14. **perspective** *(n.)* 1. a view; 2. a particular point of view

Today we can take an historical _____ on the events of 1963.

15. **precaution** *(n.)* concern taken in advance

As a _____ , wear your seat belt when riding in a car.

16. **recuperate** *(v.)* 1. to get well; 2. to get back one's health or strength

It will take time to _____ from your cold and get your energy back.

17. **shed** *(v.)* to pour or send out

She's not really sad; she is just able to _____ tears easily.

18. **stir** *(v.)* 1. to strongly affect; 2. to excite or arouse *(n.)* a great excitement

A slam dunk is a sure way to _____ the crowd's excitement.

Plans to build a mall created quite a _____ in the small town.

19. **valiant** *(adj.)* 1. brave; 2. bold; 3. fearless

The sheriff made a _____ effort to tame the Wild West town.

20. **wholesome** *(adj.)* 1. healthy; 2. good; 3. nutritious

A _____ lunch might include whole wheat bread and fruit.

Challenge Words

countenance *(n.)* a calm and approving expression *(v.)* to offer approval or permission

Her calm smile gives her a pleasing _____ .

The committee will _____ your plan to start a new club.

foremost *(adj.)* most important or first in a series of items

Tyrell was our _____ choice to receive the sportsmanship award.

nostalgia *(n.)* 1. sentimental yearning for a past period; 2. state of being homesick

I feel _____ for the days when movies were only a quarter.

orthodox *(adj.)* conforming to an established doctrine, such as a religious or political group

To join our club, you must follow our _____ way of doing things.

vigilant *(adj.)* very alert and watchful

A security guard needs to be an attentive, _____ person.

Synonyms

Synonyms are words that have the same or nearly the same meanings.

Part 1 Choose the word from the box that is the synonym for each group of words. Write the word on the line.

generate	stir	blight	inquire
precaution	shed	deter	wholesome

1. to let flow, spill, give forth _____

2. to investigate, ask, explore _____

3. a safety measure, protection, security _____

4. to discourage, stop, impede _____

5. good for you, healthful _____

6. to form, invent, originate _____

7. a disease, plague, destructive force _____

8. to energize; a commotion, uproar _____

Part 2 Replace the underlined word(s) with a word from the Basic Words list that means the same or almost the same thing. Write your answer on the line.

9. Traffic was slowed down by the <u>barrier</u> in the road. _____

10. A <u>mob</u> of autograph-seekers waited noisily at the stage door. _____

11. Al would like to be elected to a position on the <u>board</u>. _____

12. Flying bats will not <u>ensnare</u> themselves in your hair. _____

13. King Henry V encouraged his soldiers with a <u>courageous</u> speech.

_____

14. How long did it take you to <u>get better</u> after having the chicken pox?

_____

15. The best part of having a lemonade stand is the <u>splitting up</u> of the profits.

_____

Antonyms

Antonyms are words that have opposite or nearly opposite meanings.

Part 1 Choose the word from the box that is the antonym for each group of words. Write the word on the line.

inquire	valiant	generate	aerial	entangle

1. to free, unravel _____

2. cowardly, fearful, afraid _____

3. to reply, answer, respond _____

4. grounded, of the earth _____

5. to stop making, destroy _____

Part 2 Replace the underlined word(s) with a word from the Basic Words list that means the opposite or almost the opposite thing. Write your answer on the line.

6. This school pep band knows how to <u>calm</u> the students before a big game.

   _____

7. No health report can convince me that chocolate is really <u>harmful</u>.

   _____

8. Charley insisted that a real guy will <u>hold back</u> his tears. _____

9. "I think you can expect to <u>worsen</u> in the next few days," said the doctor.

   _____

10. A big fence will <u>encourage</u> everyone's plans to play in the park.

    _____

Word Study/Analogies

To complete the following analogies, decide what kind of relationship is shown by the first pair of words. Then fill in the oval next to the word that is the best choice for completing the second pair of words with the same relationship.

1. **scenic** is to **ugly** as **confident** is to _____
   - **a.** smooth
   - **b.** nervous
   - **c.** anger
   - **d.** view

2. **anger** is to **rage** as **adhere** is to _____
   - **a.** loosen
   - **b.** joy
   - **c.** attach
   - **d.** postage

3. **member** is to **council** as **player** is to _____
   - **a.** coach
   - **b.** fans
   - **c.** stadium
   - **d.** team

4. **pedestrian** is to **sidewalk** as **chauffeur** is to _____
   - **a.** cement
   - **b.** limousine
   - **c.** uniforms
   - **d.** passengers

5. **always** is to **never** as **many** is to _____
   - **a.** forever
   - **b.** much
   - **c.** obscure
   - **d.** none

Tell the Story

Choose the word from the Basic Words list that best completes each sentence. Write the word on the line. You may use the plural form of nouns and the past tense of verbs if necessary.

Cows Run Amuck as Beetle Mania Sweeps Pasture

Liverpool, Wisconsin—Farmers are suffering a terrible __1__ of shaggy-haired beetles. Yesterday, these winged, __2__ bugs suddenly landed on rocks and rolled onto the cow pastures, making a guitar and drumlike noise. The usually contented cows __3__ their common sense, screamed, and fainted. Legs and tails of swooning cows became __4__ , making it difficult for rescue workers to sort out the cows. Farmers made a courageous and __5__ effort to save their cows by carrying them into the barn.

"An event like this defies __6__ ," said the baffled governor. "It just doesn't fit into any known group of catastrophes."

The town __7__ , after a long __8__ , decided that it will take __9__ to prevent a repeat visit by this invading __10__ of beetles. A committee, searching for __11__ to __12__ insects from coming into this area, will share a __13__ of labor to get to the bottom of the problem.

"The television media is to blame for this," said the mayor. "They have __14__ a frenzy of excitement and the younger cows are easily __15__ by clever journalists making something out of nothing."

Farmer Jones said, "What we need in this country is good, __16__ bugs, not these loud bugs. Someone should get the scissors out and do something about their appearance."

To get another __17__ , this reporter approached a teen cow to __18__ about her opinion. "I think the beetles are just moovy, don't you?" she said.

All overcome cows are expected to __19__ as soon as the beetles move on. "We're playing classical music on the barn radios to __20__ these cows back to producing milk, but so far the heifers aren't responding," said the president of the dairy council.

1. _____

2. _____

3. _____

4. _____

5. _____

6. _____

7. _____

8. _____

9. _____

10. _____

11. _____

12. _____

13. _____

14. _____

15. _____

16. _____

17. _____

18. _____

19. _____

20. _____

Challenge Writing

An Artist's Plan Imagine that you are an artist planning a painting. Your painting will deal with farmers whose fields have been invaded by hordes of insects. Using the Challenge Words below, write a description of what you plan to paint. Be sure to describe the farmers' faces.

countenance	foremost	nostalgia	orthodox	vigilant

ın with Words

m is a word made by mixing up the letters of one word in order to spell another word. For instance, rearranging the letters of the word *moat* gives the anagram *atom*. The letters are the same, they're just in a different order.

In the activity below, you'll see an equation like this:

Ex: hero + d = a lot of heroes _____

The letters to the left of the equal sign are an anagram of one of the chapter vocabulary words (plus one or two additional letters that are needed to complete the vocabulary word). The words to the right of the equal sign give you a hint. In the sample above, combine the letters from the word *hero* with the letter *d* and rearrange them. You should come up with *horde,* which means a lot of people. Write the vocabulary word in the blank.

1. tree + d = trying to stop a tree _____

2. liar + ae = a flying liar _____

3. ed + beat = a formal discussion with Ed _____

4. coil + cun = a gathering of wise coils _____

5. anvil + at = a brave iron block _____

6. teenager = a kid wanting to make things happen _____

7. closet + ab = a closet that's in the way _____

8. creature + ep = a creature that's getting better _____

9. platinum + ae = this metal wants to control you _____

10. creepiest + vp = depends on how you look at it _____

Word Meanings Underline the word that is best defined by each phrase.

1. an assembly of people called together for advice
   a. corridor   **b.** beacon   **c.** division   **d.** council

2. the power or strength to endure
   a. perspective   **b.** stamina   **c.** blight   **d.** posterity

3. to move in a zigzag pattern
   a. sprawl   **b.** weave   **c.** generate   **d.** manipulate

4. actual and precise
   a. literal   **b.** serene   **c.** inevitable   **d.** urban

5. to engage in a formal argument
   a. detect   **b.** correspond   **c.** debate   **d.** deter

6. a light used as a signal or warning
   a. harbor   **b.** shaft   **c.** precaution   **d.** beacon

7. to do something in response
   a. dissolve   **b.** stir   **c.** react   **d.** gasp

8. to surround and try to take
   a. rebel   **b.** besiege   **c.** civilize   **d.** impede

9. having to do with the air
   a. aerial   **b.** literal   **c.** advisable   **d.** wholesome

10. to influence with skill or cunning
    a. pore   **b.** whisk   **c.** manipulate   **d.** distort

11. the act of giving attention to
    a. classification   **b.** precaution   **c.** persuasion   **d.** observation

12. to keep from doing something
    a. entangle   **b.** deter   **c.** detach   **d.** shed

13. the quality of being transparent
    a. initiative   **b.** stamina   **c.** clarity   **d.** nonabrasive

14. to keep something going
    a. uphold   **b.** inquire   **c.** enrage   **d.** civilize

15. something that is in the way
    a. obstacle   **b.** pedestrian   **c.** blight   **d.** shaft

16. to slash or crush badly
    a. mangle   **b.** enlist   **c.** entangle   **d.** detect

17. without definite size and shape
    a. nonabrasive   **b.** valiant   **c.** adventurous   **d.** gaseous

18. to move with light, rapid strokes
    a. whisk   **b.** dissolve   **c.** distort   **d.** obscure

19. a large number of people
    a. pedestrian   **b.** timid   **c.** horde   **d.** clarity

20. to make someone extremely angry
    a. enlist   **b.** enrage   **c.** recuperate   **d.** shed

Sentence Completion Choose the word from the box that best completes each of the following sentences. Write the word in the blank.

| serene | stir | pores | recuperated | corridors |
| posterity | gasped | harbor | inquired | impede |

1. The teacher _____ about my missing homework.

2. The _____ on an elephant's skin can easily be seen by the naked eye.

3. Once the ducks began to quack noisily, the _____ moment ended.

4. Our family takes a formal photograph every year for _____.

5. Trying to _____ Spot's rush to his bowl is like trying to stop a train.

6. Jason _____ when I jumped out in front of him.

7. The mansion had so many different _____ that I soon became lost.

8. Lydia _____ quickly from her bicycle accident.

9. The arrival of the parade floats caused quite a _____.

10. Mom said we could _____ the stray cat, but only for a few days.

Fill in the Blanks Underline the pair of words that best completes each sentence.

1. When Thomas said, "I'm hungry enough to eat a horse," his _____ younger brother was afraid he was being _____ .

    a. valiant, inevitable   **c.** timid, literal

    b. enraged, advisable   **d.** adventurous, obscure

2. Some of the ideas the _____ brought up were too _____ for the voters to understand.

   a. pedestrian, timid

   b. council, obscure

   c. horde, inevitable

   d. rebel, valiant

3. It is _____ to eat a diet of _____ foods such as fruits, vegetables, and grains.

   a. advisable, wholesome

   b. adventurous, aerial

   c. inevitable, serene

   d. civilized, nonabrasive

4. If you _____ the doctor's help, you will _____ in no time at all.

   a. mangle, stir

   b. deter, correspond

   c. enlist, recuperate

   d. impede, whisk

5. The damaged ship sailed into the _____, skillfully avoiding all _____ .

   a. corridor, observations

   b. division, shafts

   c. beacon, pedestrians

   d. harbor, obstacles

6. If you have _____ of vision and lots of _____, you will achieve your goals.

   a. clarity, stamina

   b. posterity, pores

   c. perspective, blight

   d. precaution, perspective

7. The _____ police officer dived into the _____ to save the little boy.

   a. timid, horde

   b. urban, obstacle

   c. valiant, harbor

   d. adventurous, perspective

8. The _____ of buzzing bees _____ the bull.

   a. classification, detected

   b. horde, enraged

   c. corridor, besieged

   d. blight, distorted

9. It is _____ that rush hour traffic will _____ our progress.

   a. wholesome, manipulate

   b. nonabrasive, weave

   c. valiant, distort

   d. inevitable, impede

10. The audience _____ about the subject of the _____ .

    a. gasped, obstacle

    b. inquired, debate

    c. dissolved, beacon

    d. detected, rebel

Classifying Words

Sort the words in the box by writing each word to complete a phrase in the correct category.

adventurous	aerial	beacon	council	harbor
horde	impede	observation	obstacles	pedestrians
perspective	persuasion	posterity	precaution	react
serene	stamina	timid	urban	wholesome

Words You Might Use to Talk about Outer Space

1. the moon shining like a _____ for the Apollo astronauts

2. a satellite whose purpose is the _____ of Mars

3. taking _____ photos of the earth from a spaceship

4. leaving footsteps on the moon for _____

5. taking every _____ so our astronauts will be safe

Words You Might Use to Talk about Cities

6. stopping for _____ in crosswalks

7. clearing the ice from the _____ in winter

8. committees making plans for _____ renewal

9. being elected to the city _____

10. making sure nothing will _____ ambulances

Words You Might Use to Talk about Business

11. having the _____ to put in long hours

12. using _____ to convince customers to buy

13. overcoming _____ that stand in your way

14. being ready to _____ quickly to trends in the market

15. not being too _____ to try out new ideas

Words You Might Use to Talk about Vacation

16. a _____ of people crowding the beach

17. getting outdoors in the _____ fresh air

18. an _____ ride down the river on a raft

19. seeing everything from a new _____

20. feeling peaceful and _____

Chapter 10

Word List

Read each word using the pronunciation key.

Basic Words

ailment (āl´ mənt)
boisterous (boi´ stər əs)
coax (kōks)
cringe (krinj)
determination (di tər mə nā´ shən)
distraught (dis trôt´)
dual (do͞o´ əl)
entrust (en trust´)
generator (jen´ ə rā tər)
humiliation (hyo͞o mil ē ā´ shən)
invigorate (in vig´ ə rāt)
marine (mə rēn´)
oddly (od´ lē)
parallel (pâr´ ə lel)
presume (pri zo͞om´)
relations (ri lā´ shənz)
shrill (shril)
strenuous (stren´ yo͞o əs)
variable (vâr´ ē ə bəl)
wistful (wist´ fəl)

Challenge Words

detest (di test´)
fruitless (fro͞ot´ ləs)
haggle (hag´ əl)
patronize (pā´ trə nīz)
procure (prō kyŏor´)

Word Study

Prefixes

The prefix *fore-* means *in front* or *before*.

forecast (fôr´ kast) *(n.)* a statement of what is coming
forefather (fôr´ fä ~~th~~ər) *(n.)* an ancestor
forepaw (fôr´ pô) *(n.)* a front paw
foresee (fôr´ sē) *(v.)* to know beforehand
foresight (fôr´ sīt) *(n.)* the power to know beforehand
foretell (fôr tel´) *(v.)* to predict

Be Careful!

Commonly Misspelled Words

ache	break	raise
author	delicious	straight

 # Words in Context

Read each sentence below to decipher the meaning of each boldface word. Use reasoning skills and the remainder of the sentence to help you. Write the meaning of the word on the line.

1. An **ailment**, such as the common cold, is unpleasant, but not serious.

_____

2. The bus driver asked the **boisterous** students to be quieter on the bus.

_____

3. Since David is so responsible, I will **entrust** him with the money we collected.

_____

4. The ice cream store has a backup **generator** if the electricity goes out during a storm.

_____

5. We saw crabs, starfish, and other **marine** life at the seashore aquarium.

_____

6. If you are weary, a day of hiking in the fresh mountain air will **invigorate** you.

_____

7. Gloria was filled with **determination** to finish this year's marathon race.

_____

8. In preparation for the graduation, chairs were set up in neat, **parallel** rows.

_____

9. Paula tried to **coax** her sister to the party by saying how much fun it would be.

_____

10. Mary let out a **shrill** scream when Kenji jumped out and surprised her.

_____

Word Meanings

Within each group, study the spelling, part(s) of speech, and meaning(s) of each word. Complete each sentence by writing the word on the line. Then read the sentence.

Basic Words

1. **ailment** *(n.)* a sickness, illness

   What _____ is keeping you home from school today?

2. **boisterous** *(adj.)* cheerfully loud

   Nothing is as noisy as a _____ three-year-old on her birthday.

3. **coax** *(v.)* to influence or persuade by using kindness

   Promise anything, but you will never _____ Mateo to eat spinach.

4. **cringe** *(v.)* to shrink in fear, pain, or danger

   The unexpected lion's roar caused the kindergartners to _____.

5. **determination** *(n.)* having great purpose

   The Special Olympic athletes raced with great _____.

6. **distraught** *(adj.)* irrational, upset

   Molly, _____ over losing her key, sat on the steps and wept.

7. **dual** *(adj.)* made up of two parts

   Instead of playing only one role, every actor had _____ roles in the play.

8. **entrust** *(v.)* to turn something over to someone else's care

   I _____ my best friend with my most private secrets.

9. **generator** *(n.)* a machine used to make electricity from mechanical energy

   Let's start the _____ and get the baseball field lit up.

10. **humiliation** *(n.)* a lowering of self-respect

    I felt such _____ when I tripped over the tree branch.

11. **invigorate** *(v.)* to fill with energy and life

    Does playing a soccer game _____ you or tire you out?

12. **marine** *(adj.)* 1. of or found in the sea; 2. produced by the sea *(n.)* a person serving in the United States Marine Corps (usually Marine)

An oil spill in the ocean affects the _____ life.

My father was a _____ in World War II.

13. **oddly** *(adj.)* 1. in a peculiar or unusual manner; 2. weirdly

Our dog walks _____ when we make him wear his snow boots.

14. **parallel** *(adj.)* 1. the same distance apart at every point; 2. similar

The _____ streets of Main and Elm are the east and west boundaries.

15. **presume** *(v.)* 1. to assume; 2. to take for granted

The judge told the jury to _____ the defendant's innocence.

16. **relations** *(n.)* the connection or association between persons, groups, or countries

Tourism increased when _____ improved between the countries.

17. **shrill** *(adj.)* having a sharp, high pitch or sound

The shepherd directs her dogs with a _____ , high-pitched whistle.

18. **strenuous** *(adj.)* 1. very forceful; 2. active

Running, swimming, and cycling are _____ exercise.

19. **variable** *(adj.)* 1. changeable; 2. uncertain *(n.)* something that is likely to change

You'll hear _____ amounts of noise from each classroom.

We don't know who will arrive, so it is a _____ in our plans.

20. **wistful** *(adj.)* 1. longing; 2. yearning

The child looked into the bakery window with a _____ expression.

Challenge Words

detest *(v.)* 1. to feel great dislike for; 2. to hate

"I _____ cold weather," said Cindy, who used to live in Florida.

fruitless *(adj.)* 1. lacking fruit; 2. not successful

Lucy remained locked out after a _____ search for her keys.

haggle *(v.)* 1. to bargain; 2. to argue in an attempt to come to an agreement

You can _____ at the village markets to get the best prices.

patronize *(v.)* 1. to provide frequent support for; 2. to treat condescendingly

"Madam," said the chauffeur, "I do not like it when you _____ me."

procure *(v.)* to attain with care and effort

If you would like to sit down, I will _____ a chair for you.

Synonyms

Synonyms are words that have the same or nearly the same meanings.

Part 1 Choose the word from the box that is the synonym for each group of words. Write the word on the line.

ailment	oddly	wistful	entrust
strenuous	coax	variable	humiliation

1. in a strange or irregular way _____

2. to convince, urge, encourage _____

3. a disease, disorder, complaint _____

4. something that is temporary; alterable _____

5. embarrassment, unease, shame _____

6. requiring a great deal of effort _____

7. to charge with, assign, give to _____

8. hopeful, wishing for, thoughtful _____

Part 2 Replace the underlined word(s) with a word from the Basic Words list that means the same or almost the same thing. Write your answer on the line.

9. To make her point, the senator pounded on the podium and spoke with <u>firmness</u>.

_____

10. Eating a good breakfast will <u>energize</u> you for the day ahead.

_____

11. The <u>worried</u> look on Trinh's face told us something was wrong. _____

12. A bunch of <u>noisy, rowdy</u> boys rushed from the locker room and onto the field.

_____

13. With twins, the new parents had to get <u>duplicate</u> strollers, cribs, and car seats.

_____

14. <u>Attachments</u> between teachers and their students have never been better.

_____

15. When the two explorers met, one said to the other, "Dr. Livingston, I <u>conclude</u>?"

_____

Antonyms

Antonyms are words that have opposite or nearly opposite meanings.

Part 1 Choose the word from the box that is the antonym for each group of words. Write the word on the line.

| coax | oddly | variable |
| distraught | entrust | shrill |

1. normally, in a familiar way   _____

2. to discourage, deter, curb   _____

3. stable, predictable; a constant   _____

4. to withdraw, withhold, refuse   _____

5. having a dull, low sound   _____

6. comfortable, happy, at peace   _____

Part 2 Replace the underlined word(s) with a word from the Basic Words list that means the opposite or almost the opposite thing. Write your answer on the line.

7. There is a committee investigating the <u>detachment</u> of the two rival schools.

_____

8. Ana is looking for an <u>effortless</u> activity to occupy her after school.

_____

9. Carlos thinks a half hour on the exercise machines will <u>weaken</u> him.

_____

10. That hat will only bring you <u>a rise in the opinion of yourself</u>.

_____

11. The triplets were living <u>different</u> lives in different cities. _____

# **Word Study**/Prefixes

Add the prefix *fore-* to these words. Then use each new word in a sentence.

1. cast _____

_____

_____

2. father _____

_____

_____

3. paw _____

_____

_____

4. see _____

_____

_____

5. sight _____

_____

_____

6. tell _____

_____

_____

Tell the Story

Choose the word from the Basic Words list that best completes each sentence. Write the word on the line. You may use the plural form of nouns and the past tense of verbs if necessary.

To help build good __1__ between our community and those who serve it, a park ranger visited our class. He spoke enthusiastically about the variety of __2__ life found along the shores of our state. The ranger explained that the number of tourists visiting our beaches was __3__ from season to season.

The ranger answered questions about the ocean and shore environment, but he __4__ when someone asked about the effect of oil spills. He seemed __5__ when he told us that he worries about the harm caused by accidental spills. For example, he told us that chemicals and oil in the water have caused a number of serious __6__ in birds and other shore animals. The ranger said, "The care of our planet has been __7__ to us, so we should try to keep Earth clean and healthy."

In a(n) __8__ voice, he spoke of his desire to stroll on a clean beach. "I want our beach to be a source of pride and not __9__ , so I've organized a beach cleanup day," the ranger said. "May I __10__ that everyone will join our cleanup efforts?" He did not need to __11__ us to join. We were eager to help.

On cleanup day, we approached the task with __12__ . We organized ourselves into __13__ lines across the beach to thoroughly cover the area. Then we walked along, picking up litter and putting it in a bag. It was enjoyable, and not at all __14__ work. In fact, the cool breeze helped to __15__ us. The __16__ cries of the seagulls flying overhead reminded us that we were helping many animals.

What a(n) __17__ group we were, laughing and chatting as we picked up trash. We were so purposeful that no one goofed off or behaved __18__ . We stopped at dusk, but would have continued if we had had a power __19__ to provide lights. Our work served a(n) __20__ purpose—we cleaned up our beach and made a new friend.

1. _____

2. _____

3. _____

4. _____

5. _____

6. _____

7. _____

8. _____

9. _____

10. _____

11. _____

12. _____

13. _____

14. _____

15. _____

16. _____

17. _____

18. _____

19. _____

20. _____

Challenge Writing

The Daily News You work for a newspaper. Your job is to write an editorial on a local environmental issue, using the Challenge Words below. On a separate sheet of paper, explain the problem, give your opinion, and suggest what your readers can do to help solve the problem. Try to persuade your readers to agree with you.

detest	fruitless	haggle	patronize	procure

Fun with Words

Choose six of the following eight words. Write a paragraph in which you use the words to describe someone you know.

boisterous   coax   determination   entrust
invigorate   presume   oddly   wistful

_____

_____

_____

_____

_____

_____

_____

_____

_____

_____

_____

_____

_____

_____

Chapter 11

Word List

Read each word using the pronunciation key.

Basic Words

ajar (ə jär´)
bombard (bom bärd´)
bough (bou)
collaborate (kə lab´ ə rāt)
criticism (krit´ i siz əm)
diameter (dī am´ i tər)
duplicate (*n., adj.* dōō´pli kit)
  (*v.* dōō´ pli kāt)
epidemic (ep i dem´ ik)
geologist (jē ol´ ə jist)
hustle (hus´ əl)
invalid (in val´ id)
irrational (i rash´ ə nəl)
maul (môl)
ointment (oint´ mənt)
prevail (pre vāl´)
reliance (re lī´ əns)
signify (sig´ nə fī)
stupefy (stōō´ pə fī)
variation (vâr ē ā´ shən)
wondrous (wun´ drəs)

Challenge Words

diminish (di min´ ish)
goad (gōd)
heed (hēd)
insistent (in sis´ tənt)
oppress (ə pres´)

Word Study

Suffixes

The suffix *-ous* means *full of* or *having much*.

courageous (kə rā´ jəs) *(adj.)* brave

dangerous (dān´ jər əs) *(n.)* not safe

humorous (hyü´ mər əs) *(adj.)* funny

joyous (joi´ əs) *(adj.)* joyful, glad

ridiculous (ri dik´ yə ləs) *(adj.)* laughable

suspicious (sə spish´ əs) *(adj.)* questionable

Be Careful!

Commonly Misspelled Words

shoes	sure	tear
sugar	dear	wear

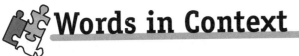 **Words in Context**

Read each sentence below to decipher the meaning of each boldface word. Use reasoning skills and the remainder of the sentence to help you. Write the meaning of the word on the line.

1. We'll really have to **hustle** to get to the movie on time.

_____

2. Please leave the door **ajar** so I can hear the baby if she cries.

_____

3. Will the three of you **collaborate** to finish the science project?

_____

4. Mrs. Post showed her **reliance** on me by appointing me to be fire marshal.

_____

5. I put my name on the petition to **signify** my agreement.

_____

6. The colors and grandeur of the Grand Canyon are a **wondrous** sight.

_____

7. An **epidemic** of measles spread through several cities.

_____

8. I will make a **duplicate** of the story I wrote in case I lose the original.

_____

9. The company's **geologist** studies the earth's crust to help find oil.

_____

10. The construction worker used a **maul** to drive the heavy stakes into the ground.

_____

Word Meanings

Within each group, study the spelling, part(s) of speech, and meaning(s) of each word. Complete each sentence by writing the word on the line. Then read the sentence.

Basic Words

1. **ajar** *(adj.)* partially open

   Rachel left the basement door _____ so that the cat can come in.

2. **bombard** *(v.)* to continually attack with great force

   The press will _____ the police chief with questions.

3. **bough** *(n.)* a branch of a tree

   The tree surgeon needed a ladder and a saw to trim the top _____ .

4. **collaborate** *(v.)* to work cooperatively with others

   Five or six students can _____ to finish their assignments.

5. **criticism** *(n.)* negative statements or opinions

   The actor never reads reviews because he is sensitive to _____.

6. **diameter** *(n.)* 1. a straight line that runs through the center of a circle or sphere; 2. the width or thickness of something that is circular

   This pipe has an opening that is six inches in _____ .

7. **duplicate** *(n.)* a copy, clone, double *(adj.)* exactly the same as something else *(v.)* 1. to copy something exactly; 2. to reproduce

   Can you tell which is the _____ and which is the original?

   The sisters dressed in _____ sweatshirts.

   The sculptor was commissioned to _____ the original statue.

8. **epidemic** *(n.)* the quick spreading of a disease that affects many people at once

   In the nineteenth century, an outbreak of flu was a dangerous

   _____ .

9. **geologist** *(n.)* an expert in the science of the earth's structure and history

   A _____ spoke to our science class about the earth's formation.

10. **hustle** *(v.)* to hurry or move quickly *(n.)* hurried action or motion

    Viola was late for dinner and had to _____ to be on time.

    Trains and traffic add to the _____ and bustle of the big city.

11. **invalid** *(adj.)* 1. not true; 2. not sound

    Due to lack of information, the jury made an _____ decision.

12. **irrational** *(adj.)* not sensible or reasonable

    There is no explanation for Kirsten's _____ behavior.

13. **maul** *(n.)* a heavy hammer or mallet *(v.)* to beat or handle roughly

    Abe Lincoln used a _____ and a wedge to split logs into rails.

    Keep the cat away so she won't _____ the fragile material.

14. **ointment** *(n.)* a greasy substance used to heal the skin or to make it soft

    Apply this _____ to the cut on your hand to help it heal.

15. **prevail** *(v.)* to succeed or win

    We expect last year's winner to _____ again in the tournament.

16. **reliance** *(n.)* trust, faith, confidence

    Dad's _____ on the old car keeps him from getting a new one.

17. **signify** *(v.)* to indicate by signs, words, or actions

    This card will _____ your membership and admit you to the club.

18. **stupefy** *(v.)* 1. to stun, dull the senses of; 2. to amaze

    See the amazing circus high-wire act. It will _____ you.

19. **variation** *(n.)* 1. a change; 2. a different form

    A cold day in Phoenix is a _____ in the normal weather.

20. **wondrous** *(adj.)* wonderful

    The entire graduating class in caps and gowns is a _____ sight.

Challenge Words

diminish *(v.)* 1. to decrease or make less; 2. to dwindle

We waited for the rain to _____ so we wouldn't get wet.

goad *(n.)* something that urges someone into action *(v.)* to urge into action

Ranchers use a _____ , a pointed stick, to drive cattle on.

Asking for money over the phone might _____ people into donating.

heed *(v.)* to pay attention to

If you don't _____ my advice, you'll be making a mistake.

insistent *(adj.)* 1. holds attention; 2. persistent

The _____ dog refused to stop barking until it got its food.

oppress *(v.)* 1. to crush or burden by abusing power; 2. to burden physically or spiritually by abusing power

A dictator can _____ people by taking away their rights.

Synonyms

Synonyms are words that have the same or nearly the same meanings.

Part 1 Choose the word from the box that is the synonym for each group of words. Write the word on the line.

criticism	ointment	bough	prevail
epidemic	variation	reliance	bombard

1. a salve, balm, lotion _____

2. an alteration, deviation, difference _____

3. to blitz, assault, charge _____

4. an outbreak, plague _____

5. a limb, a shoot _____

6. to triumph, achieve victory _____

7. a disapproving comment _____

8. a dependence, assurance, certainty _____

Part 2 Replace the underlined word(s) with a word from the Basic Words list that means the same or almost the same thing. Write your answer on the line.

9. The protesters say it is <u>senseless</u> to cut down old elm trees just to widen a road.

_____

10. At an auction, you can <u>communicate</u> your bid with just a nod of your head.

_____

11. To keep our dog from chewing shoes, we give him a rawhide toy to <u>mangle</u>

instead. _____

12. "Our game strategy," said the coach, "will be to <u>rush</u> the other team's quarterback."

_____

13. The noisy arrival of barnstorming airplanes would <u>astonish</u> the folks on the

ground. _____

14. You'll need tickets if you want to hear our <u>marvelous</u> symphony orchestra.

_____

15. Please correct any <u>false</u> information on your student identification.

_____

Antonyms

Antonyms are words that have opposite or nearly opposite meanings.

Part 1 Choose the word from the box that is the antonym for each group of words. Write the word on the line.

prevail	irrational	collaborate	ajar	reliance

1. closed, shut, blocked _____

2. to work independently _____

3. to fail, lose, be defeated _____

4. a doubt, misgiving, suspicion _____

5. showing good judgment _____

Part 2 Replace the underlined word(s) with a word from the Basic Words list that means the opposite or almost the opposite thing. Write your answer on the line.

6. Customers always <u>dawdle</u> around the magazine rack in the bookstore.

_____

7. Frank's photographs told a story of a very <u>ordinary</u> vacation. _____

8. Make a copy of your story on the copy machine and then give me the <u>original</u>.

_____

9. The <u>similarity</u> among the sweaters made it difficult to choose which one to wear.

_____

10. The dancers held their breath as they waited to hear their instructor's <u>praise</u>.

_____

Word Study/Suffixes

Write the words from the box that have these meanings and suffixes.

courageous	humorous	ridiculous
dangerous	joyous	suspicious

1. chance of harm + ous = _____

2. doubt + ous = _____

3. gladness + ous = _____

4. bravery + ous = _____

5. make fun of + ous = _____

6. funny + ous = _____

Challenge Writing

Thank You Very Much Imagine that a favorite friend or relative has taken you along on an adventurous journey. On a separate sheet of paper, write a thank-you note to this person, using the Challenge Words below. Be sure to describe where the journey took place and what happened along the way.

diminish	goad	heed	insistent	oppress

Tell the Story

Choose the word from the Basic Words list that best completes each sentence. Write the word on the line. You may use the plural form of nouns and the past tense of verbs if necessary.

My Aunt Dora, a(n) __1__ and athletic rock climber, invited me to go rock climbing with her. At first I thought this was a(n) __2__ idea because I had already planned to spend my summer mowing lawns to earn extra money. Aunt Dora said she would not accept my __3__ excuses. She said I could mow lawns any summer, but how often would I get invited to go rock climbing? She said that she would leave the door of opportunity __4__ but I would be sorry if I did not take advantage of her offer. Aunt Dora thinks that nothing short of a deadly __5__ should keep a person from climbing rocks in the great outdoors. She continued to __6__ me with reasons as to why I should go until she __7__ , and I agreed to go.

I had very little rock-climbing experience, so my __8__ on Aunt Dora's expertise was great. She encouraged me gently, not being one to give harsh __9__ . She was patient as she showed me simple climbing techniques, but she saved the more difficult __10__ for herself. She would __11__ me with her __12__ climbing ability as she leaped from ledge to ledge with grace and skill.

We had to __13__ to solve any climbing problem. We had to cross a deep gully by swinging from a low __14__ of a nearby tree. First, Aunt Dora carefully estimated the __15__ of the branch to make sure it was thick enough to hold our weight. Then she swung over. I waved to her to __16__ that I was ready to cross. But when I tried to __17__ her graceful movements, I was not quite so successful. I landed clumsily and yelped in pain, thinking I had __18__ my leg. Aunt Dora calmly examined me and said I had only scratched my ankle. She applied a(n) __19__ that eased the sting of my wound. Next summer I'd rather __20__ behind the lawn mower than swing down a canyon wall.

1. _____
2. _____
3. _____
4. _____
5. _____
6. _____
7. _____
8. _____
9. _____
10. _____
11. _____
12. _____
13. _____
14. _____
15. _____
16. _____
17. _____
18. _____
19. _____
20. _____

Fun with Words

Study the word web. Complete the sentences with words from this chapter. Then, write a paragraph about a problem you have solved.

Don't _____ . Slow down and think things through.

_____ with others to find a solution.

_____ actions that have worked in the past.

Try not to be _____, even if you're angry.

Ways to Deal with Difficulties

_____ to others that you are working on improving the situation.

Try to learn something from others' _____ .

Be patient as you continue your efforts and you will _____ .

_____ on yourself is good, but don't be bossy.

_____

_____

_____

_____

_____

_____

_____

_____

_____

Word List

Read each word using the pronunciation key.

Basic Words

acknowledge (ak nol´ ij)
alibi (al´ ə bī)
bore (bôr)
commemorate (kə mem´ ə rāt)
debut (dā byo͞o´)
digestion (dī jes´ chən)
drought (drout)
duration (do͝o rā´ shən)
erupt (i rupt´)
gloat (glōt)
hypocrite (hip´ ə krit)
irregular (i reg´ yə lər)
mental (men´ təl)
oracle (ôr´ ə kəl)
prevention (pre ven´ shən)
reservoir (rez´ ər vwär)
simmer (sim´ ər)
sturdy (stər´ dē)
vast (vast)
wrangle (raŋ´ gəl)

Challenge Words

elongate (ē loŋ´ gāt)
indispensable (in di spens´ ə bəl)
lubricate (lo͞o´ bri kāt)
pending (pen´ diŋ)
unscathed (un skāthd´)

Word Study

Prefixes

The prefix *over-* means *beyond* or *too much.*

overcharge (ō vər charj´) *(v.)* to charge too much
overcooked (ō vər ko͝okt´) *(adj.)* cooked too much
overflow (ō vər flō´) *(v.)* to cover or flood
overload (ō vər lōd´) *(v.)* to load too heavily
overpay (ō vər pā´) *(v.)* to pay too much
oversleep (ō vər slēp´) *(v.)* to sleep beyond a time

Be Careful!

Commonly Misspelled Words

write	personal	government
writing	personnel	governor

# Words in Context

Read each sentence below to decipher the meaning of each boldface word. Use reasoning skills and the remainder of the sentence to help you. Write the meaning of the word on the line.

1. The statue of Albert Einstein will **commemorate** his great contributions to physics.

   _____

2. What **prevention** can you take to keep accidents from happening in your home?

   _____

3. This recipe says that tomato sauce should **simmer** over a low heat for two hours.

   _____

4. Ralph can be a **bore** when he tells his long, dull stories about his job.

   _____

5. Several witnesses back up the man's **alibi** that he was at home at 9 o'clock.

   _____

6. I've been anxiously awaiting the **debut** of the new mystery series on TV.

   _____

7. Much of the southwestern United States is a grand, **vast** desert area.

   _____

8. If we don't get rain soon, this summer will be officially declared a **drought**.

   _____

9. Many ancient plays speak of an **oracle** who could predict future events.

   _____

10. Scientists can often give a warning as to when a volcano will **erupt**.

   _____

Word Meanings

Within each group, study the spelling, part(s) of speech, and meaning(s) of each word. Complete each sentence by writing the word on the line. Then read the sentence.

Basic Words

1. **acknowledge** *(v.)* 1. to recognize; 2. to admit; 3. to concede

   Randy's parents were unhappy to hear him _____ his guilt.

2. **alibi** *(n.)* 1. a statement from an accused person claiming to be elsewhere when a crime was committed; 2. an excuse

   The burglar had an airtight _____, so the police let him go.

3. **bore** *(n.)* a wearisome, dull person or thing *(v.)* to make a hole by pushing, twisting, or digging

   The movie was a _____, so we left halfway through it.

   The handyman used a drill to _____ a peephole into the front door.

4. **commemorate** *(v.)* to honor the memory of someone or something

   The memorial service will _____ the late mayor's life.

5. **debut** *(n.)* the first presentation of someone or something *(v.)* to make a first appearance

   All of Gary's family and friends came to see his acting _____.

   The new play will _____ at an off-Broadway theater.

6. **digestion** *(n.)* the process in which food is changed in the stomach and intestines so that the body can use it

   Exercise and healthy eating will promote good _____.

7. **drought** *(n.)* 1. a period of dryness; 2. a long time without rain

   The farmers are irrigating to help the crops survive the _____.

8. **duration** *(n.)* the length of time in which something occurs

   The _____ of the school year is about nine to ten months.

9. **erupt** *(v.)* to explode with great force

   Geologists want to know what caused the volcano to _____.

10. **gloat** *(v.)* to think with pleasure about something unfortunate that happened to someone else or something good that happened to oneself

    It's impolite to _____ , even if you did beat your opponent.

11. **hypocrite** *(n.)* a person who expresses feelings or beliefs that he or she really doesn't believe in

    The candidate was accused of being a _____ just to win votes.

12. **irregular** *(adj.)* 1. not being or acting according to rule; 2. out of normal order; 3. uneven

    The floor tiles were placed in an unusual, _____ pattern.

13. **mental** *(adj.)* 1. of or by the mind; 2. having an illness of the mind

    This hospital is for patients suffering from _____ confusion.

14. **oracle** *(n.)* a person through which a god is believed to speak

    It was believed that the _____ at Delphi spoke wisely.

15. **prevention** *(n.)* 1. a keeping from happening; 2. a hindering

    Our local firefighter talked to us about fire _____.

16. **reservoir** *(n.)* a place where water is stored for future use

    The dam creates a _____ that supplies water to the desert.

17. **simmer** *(v.)* to keep the temperature just below the boiling point

    Turn the burner to low and _____ the stew in the pot.

18. **sturdy** *(adj.)* 1. strong; 2. well-built

    With seven boys in the family, the Olsens need _____ furniture.

19. **vast** *(adj.)* 1. extremely large; 2. immense

    To cross Russia, you will cover a _____ distance by train.

20. **wrangle** *(v.)* to quarrel in a noisy or angry way

    The boys always _____ over who will play the video game next.

Challenge Words

elongate *(v.)* to make longer or extend the length of

You can _____ a rubber band by pulling it.

indispensable *(adj.)* necessary or essential

Presents are _____ parts of a birthday party.

lubricate *(v.)* 1. to make smooth; 2. to supply moisture

Do we have more oil to _____ this machinery?

pending *(adj.)* not yet decided or determined

The result of the _____ decision may affect our neighborhood.

unscathed *(adj.)* not harmed or injured

Everyone else was hurt in the accident, but I was _____.

Synonyms

Synonyms are words that have the same or nearly the same meanings.

Part 1 Choose the word from the box that is the synonym for each group of words. Write the word on the line.

simmer	hypocrite	erupt	commemorate
prevention	sturdy	bore	acknowledge

1. a stopping prohibition, deterrence _____

2. to confess, own up to; to confirm _____

3. solid, rugged, hearty _____

4. to pay tribute to _____

5. to blast, blow up, burst _____

6. a fraud, faker, deceiver _____

7. to warm, cook at a low heat   _____

8. a tiresome person; to drill   _____

Part 2 Replace the underlined word(s) with a word from the Basic Words list that means the same or almost the same thing. Write your answer on the line.

9. After much rehearsal, the triumphant band had earned the right to <u>brag</u>.

   _____

10. The <u>introduction</u> of the new cars will take place at the auto show.

   _____

11. The <u>period of time</u> of the junior high basketball game is usually 24 minutes.

   _____

12. The <u>prophet</u> foretold the future in riddles that no one could understand.

   _____

13. Imagine how <u>enormous</u> the ocean must look to someone flying high in the sky.

   _____

14. Today, the seventh grade has an <u>odd</u> schedule of short class periods.

   _____

15. The cowboys are starting to <u>brawl</u> again over who gets to ride the horse.

   _____

Antonyms

Antonyms are words that have opposite or nearly opposite meanings.

Part 1 Choose the word from the box that is the antonym for each group of words. Write the word on the line.

hypocrite	drought	commemorate	sturdy	vast

1. a flood, downpour, rainy season   _____

2. a person who is honest and sincere   _____

3. tiny, slight, small   _____

4. flimsy, feeble, weak   _____

5. to discredit, dishonor   _____

Part 2 Replace the underlined word(s) with a word from the Basic Words list that means the opposite or almost the opposite thing. Write your answer on the line.

6. The baseball took an unpredictable hop on the <u>smooth</u> playing field.

_____

7. These long hikes are an unexpected <u>physical</u> challenge. _____

8. After you put in the noodles, allow the water to <u>boil furiously</u>. _____

9. Jordan wondered if it was a good idea to <u>agree</u> with his wrestling coach.

_____

10. Do you <u>deny</u> that you used to like broccoli when you were little?

_____

Word Study/Prefixes

Write the word from the box to complete each person's statement.

overcharge	overflow	overpay
overcooked	overload	oversleep

1. The butcher: I always carefully weigh each order and I never _____ my customers.

2. The chef: If by mistake we have _____ noodles, then we will make kugel.

3. The engineer: We want to build the levy here so that if the rivers

   _____ , the water won't reach the homes.

4. The truck driver: It's a law. I never _____ the vehicle beyond its lawful capacity.

5. The shopper: I shop only for what I need, I check out the bargain table, and I

   never _____ for anything.

6. The student: Even though I set my alarm clock, I still _____ and arrive late for school.

Tell the Story

Choose the word from the Basic Words list that best completes each sentence. Write the word on the line. You may use the plural form of nouns and the past tense of verbs if necessary.

Memorial Day is a holiday to __1__ all those in the armed services who served our country. Although Memorial Day is a serious, important event, it's still fun and not a(n) __2__ in our town. Our mayor gave a speech of about 15 minutes in __3__ . He gratefully __4__ the sacrifices made by so many people to preserve liberty in this country. His description of his experiences as a soldier gave me a clear __5__ picture of Europe during World War II.

This celebration was particularly special, as our new town chorus made its singing __6__ . The crowd __7__ into applause. Then the big town picnic was held at the __8__ . It was pleasant near the man-made lake, even though the recent __9__ has kept the water level too low for boating. Everyone brings a special dish to share, so we end up with __10__ amounts of different foods to enjoy. People eat as much as their __11__ can handle. Everyone looks forward to Mrs. King's baked beans. She likes to __12__ the beans on the stove and tease us with the wonderful smell long before the picnic. Adults and kids jokingly push each other and __13__ to be the first in line for Mrs. King's beans.

I sat on a not-too-__14__ lawn chair and ended up on the ground with a plateful of food in my lap. I think my brother had something to do with it, but he claimed to have a(n) __15__ about being in the food line when the chair collapsed. He showed great concern for my well-being, but I think he was being a(n) __16__ , because later I heard him __17__ over how silly I looked with my dinner all over me. I'm not surprised—it would be __18__ if my brother did not play a trick on me.

It was pretty much a perfect day except for the weather. If we had a(n) __19__ who could accurately tell us the weather, we might have brought jackets as a(n) __20__ against being uncomfortable in the cold.

1. _____
2. _____
3. _____
4. _____
5. _____
6. _____
7. _____
8. _____
9. _____
10. _____
11. _____
12. _____
13. _____
14. _____
15. _____
16. _____
17. _____
18. _____
19. _____
20. _____

Challenge Writing

I'm an Ant Imagine that you are an ant searching for food in a park where people are picnicking. On a separate sheet of paper, write a short story about your search for food, using the Challenge Words below. Be sure to describe how things smell, taste, and sound from your insect point of view.

elongate	indispensable	lubricate	pending	unscathed

Fun with Words

Read the first pair of words after each numeral and think about the connection between them. Write a word from the list below in each blank to create a similar connection between the second pair of words.

reservoir	sturdy	irregular	bore
vast	hypocrite	digestion	drought
oracle	simmer		

1. **heart** is to **circulation** as **stomach** is to _____

2. **hot** is to **cold** as **flood** is to _____

3. **spokesperson** is to **company** as _____ is to a **god**

4. **sand** is to **beach** as **water** is to _____

5. **smooth** is to **flat** as **uneven** is to _____

6. **gentle** is to **rough** as **fragile** is to _____

7. **bake** is to **cake** as _____ is to **soup**

8. **criminal** is to **crime** as _____ is to **fraud**

9. **knit** is to **sweater** as _____ is to **hole**

10. **puddle** is to **small** as **ocean** is to _____

Review 10-12

Word Meanings Underline the word that is best defined by each phrase.

1. to admit something is true
   a. bore   **b.** hustle   **c.** entrust   **d.** acknowledge

2. remarkable, fabulous, marvelous
   a. irrational   **b.** wondrous   **c.** mental   **d.** oddly

3. to enliven and excite
   a. invigorate   **b.** erupt   **c.** maul   **d.** gloat

4. to encourage in a friendly way
   a. debut   **b.** bombard   **c.** coax   **d.** cringe

5. to combine efforts
   a. simmer   **b.** stupefy   **c.** erupt   **d.** collaborate

6. troubled or distressed
   a. strenuous   **b.** distraught   **c.** diameter   **d.** parallel

7. to accomplish a goal
   a. wrangle   **b.** commemorate   **c.** duplicate   **d.** prevail

8. built in a solid way
   a. ajar   **b.** sturdy   **c.** marine   **d.** shrill

9. showing longing
   a. wistful   **b.** variable   **c.** dual   **d.** invalid

10. how long something lasts
    a. duration   **b.** reservoir   **c.** epidemic   **d.** bough

11. a bodily disorder
    a. alibi   **b.** drought   **c.** ailment   **d.** generator

12. the act of trusting
    a. epidemic   **b.** reliance   **c.** criticism   **d.** ointment

13. a stopping or deterring
    a. digestion   **b.** oracle   **c.** geologist   **d.** prevention

14. noisy in a happy, active way
    a. irregular   **b.** ajar   **c.** boisterous   **d.** distraught

15. to communicate or express
    a. signify   **b.** prevail   **c.** acknowledge   **d.** presume

16. huge in size
    a. shrill   **b.** boisterous   **c.** wistful   **d.** vast

17. one who is a pretender
    a. duration   **b.** hypocrite   **c.** relations   **d.** determination

18. to suppose or believe
    a. coax   **b.** wrangle   **c.** presume   **d.** hustle

19. to draw back in reaction to being scared or hurt
    a. cringe   **b.** invigorate   **c.** signify   **d.** gloat

20. a difference from what was planned or expected
    a. diameter   **b.** variation   **c.** alibi   **d.** ailment

Sentence Completion Choose the word from the box that best completes each of the following sentences. Write the word in the blank.

bore	simmer	invalid	strenuous	debut
entrust	criticism	epidemic	duplicate	determination

1. I'd really like to attend the _____ of the ten-year-old violinist on Friday night.

2. Doctors are working to prevent the spread of the disease so that it doesn't become a(n) _____ .

3. Many people have succeeded through hard work and _____ .

4. I find stamp collecting interesting, but my friends think it's a(n)

   _____ .

5. Most people respond better to praise than they do to _____ .

6. How long should the sauce _____ before we add the vegetables?

7. Jill's argument was basically sound, but she did make a few _____ points.

8. Raking leaves is very _____ work.

9. May I _____ your famous cherry pie recipe?

10. Janet knew better than to _____ her baseball card collection to her brother.

Fill in the Blanks
Underline the pair of words that best completes each sentence.

1. Sharla _____ at the sound of the _____ crowd.
   a. coaxed, epidemic
   b. simmered, duplicate
   c. presumed, wondrous
   d. cringed, boisterous

2. Leesa was _____ about the _____ accusation.
   a. distraught, irrational
   b. sturdy, shrill
   c. wistful, vast
   d. stupefied, ajar

3. Believe it or not, _____ exercise can _____ you.
   a. variable, coax
   b. strenuous, invigorate
   c. invalid, simmer
   d. irregular, commemorate

4. Ali _____ he would be allowed to _____ with Gino on the science project.
   a. entrusted, stupefy
   b. acknowledged, gloat
   c. wrangled, prevail
   d. presumed, collaborate

5. The _____ swore he had a(n) _____ for the time of the theft.
   a. Marine, ointment
   b. geologist, alibi
   c. generator, epidemic
   d. hypocrite, debut

6. There is practically no _____ between the original and the _____ .
   a. criticism, oracle
   b. diameter, reservoir
   c. determination, bore
   d. variation, duplicate

7. The speaker refused to _____ the audience's _____ .
   a. commemorate, duration
   b. hustle, variation
   c. acknowledge, criticism
   d. gloat, reliance

8. Keep your skis _____ if you want to avoid the _____ of sprawling in the snow.
   a. parallel, humiliation
   b. ajar, prevention
   c. boisterous, digestion
   d. duplicate, variation

9. School was closed for the _____ of the _____ .
   a. bough, reservoir
   b. duration, epidemic
   c. relations, ailment
   d. criticism, variations

10. The _____ says she can see a(n) _____ picture of future events.
    a. ointment, wondrous
    b. debut, irregular
    c. bore, wistful
    d. oracle, mental

Classifying Words
Sort the words in the box by writing each word to complete a phrase in the correct category.

acknowledge	ailment	criticism	debut	determination
diameter	droughts	erupt	geologist	gloat
invigorated	irrational	marine	ointment	prevention
reservoir	sturdy	variable	variations	vast

Words You Might Use to Talk about Health and Safety

1. the old saying that an ounce of _____ is worth a pound of cure

2. climbing on a ladder that is strong and _____

3. seeing the doctor at the first sign of an _____

4. a brisk walk that makes you feel _____

5. an antiseptic _____ in the first aid kit

Words You Might Use to Talk about Acting

6. bowing to _____ applause from the audience

7. making your _____ in a Broadway play

8. not letting thoughtless _____ upset you

9. trying hard not to _____ when they call you a star

10. holding on to your _____ when you don't get a part

Words You Might Use to Talk about Earth

11. the _____ who learns the earth's history from rocks

12. volcanoes that _____ without any warning

13. a formula for measuring the _____ of the planet

14. trying to predict earthquakes, floods, and _____

15. enjoying the _____ of the seasons

Words You Might Use to Talk about Water

16. the _____ that holds a city's supply of drinking water

17. snorkeling to come face to face with _____ creatures

18. trying to sail in _____ winds

19. an _____ fear of little minnows

20. standing on shore looking at the _____ ocean

Chapter 13

Word List

Read each word using the pronunciation key.

Basic Words

altitude (al´ ti to͞od)
broker (brō´ kər)
commence (kə mens´)
compact (kəm pakt´)
dedicate (ded´ ə kāt)
digestive (dī jes´ tiv)
eavesdrop (ēvz´ drop)
evolve (i vôlv´)
glorify (glôr´ ə fī)
hypodermic (hī pə dər´ mik)
irritable (ir´ ə tə bəl)
metallic (mə tal´ ik)
ovation (o vā´ shən)
principle (prin´ sə pəl)
resign (ri zīn´)
schedule (skej´ o͝ol)
simulate (sim´ yo͞o lāt)
submissive (səb mis´ iv)
veil (vāl)
writhe (rīth)

Challenge Words

interrogate (in târ´ ə gāt)
melancholy (mel´ ən käl ē)
pervade (pər vād´)
stalemate (stāl´ māt)
transcribe (tran skrīb´)

Word Study

Analogies

Analogies show relationships between pairs of words. Study the relationships between the pairs of words in the analogies below.

bed is to **sleep** as **chair** is to **sit**

ring is to **finger** as **watch** is to **wrist**

den is to **fox** as **cave** is to **bat**

Be Careful!

Commonly Misspelled Words

either	fundamental	nickel
original	quarrel	typical

 # Words in Context

Read each sentence below to decipher the meaning of each boldface word. Use reasoning skills and the remainder of the sentence to help you. Write the meaning of the word on the line.

1. We hired a real estate **broker** to help us sell our house.

_____

2. The hot air balloon lifted us to an **altitude** of 1,200 feet above sea level.

_____

3. At the end of the splendid concert, the band received a standing **ovation**.

_____

4. A **veil** of fog hid the football field from the spectators' view.

_____

5. I think tomato juice from a can has a **metallic** taste.

_____

6. How can you tell the leader of the pack from the more **submissive** wolves?

_____

7. Sharon picked up the phone extension to **eavesdrop** on her sister's conversation.

_____

8. If I don't eat breakfast, I am a crabby and **irritable** person by midmorning.

_____

9. Bob **resigned** from his job so he could return to his college studies.

_____

10. The stomach and small and large intestines are parts of the **digestive** system.

_____

Word Meanings

Within each group, study the spelling, part(s) of speech, and meaning(s) of each word. Complete each sentence by writing the word on the line. Then read the sentence.

Basic Words

1. **altitude** *(n.)* the level or height above the surface of the earth

   Our mountain hike took us to an _____ of 6,000 feet.

2. **broker** *(n.)* a person who is hired to buy or sell things for other people

   The antique _____ offered $90 for our grandmother's gravy bowl.

3. **commence** *(v.)* 1. to start; 2. to begin

   We'll _____ the pie-eating contest when I say "go!"

4. **compact** *(adj.)* packed tightly together *(v.)* to pack or press tightly

   Roll your sleeping bag into a _____ bundle.

   We can get all the luggage into the trunk if we _____ it.

5. **dedicate** *(v.)* to commit or devote to something specific

   It's romantic to have someone _____ a special song to you.

6. **digestive** *(adj.)* having to do with the process of digestion

   The _____ system is the next chapter in our health book.

7. **eavesdrop** *(v.)* to listen in secret to the conversations of others

   Sara hid in the closet in order to _____ on the conversation.

8. **evolve** *(v.)* to develop or grow gradually

   Over time, the boys' rivalry will _____ into a strong friendship.

9. **glorify** *(v.)* 1. to give honor to; 2. to make distinguished; 3. to worship or praise

   New York had a big parade to _____ the returning astronauts.

10. **hypodermic** *(adj.)* injected or used to inject beneath the skin

The nurse brought out a _____ needle and Ty nearly fainted.

11. **irritable** *(adj.)* 1. easily made angry; 2. impatient; 3. oversensitive

A tired and _____ baby needs to be put to bed for a nap.

12. **metallic** *(adj.)* 1. of or composed of metal; 2. like metal

The shimmer in the fabric was caused by its _____ threads.

13. **ovation** *(n.)* an expression of approval or enjoyment by enthusiastic applause

The Republicans sat quietly while the Democrats gave an _____ .

14. **principle** *(n.)* a basic rule or standard

Honesty is a highly valued _____ at the military academy.

15. **resign** *(v.)* 1. to give up a job; 2. to quit

Ill health has caused our librarian to _____ from her position.

16. **schedule** *(n.)* a written list of events or appointments *(v.)* to set the time for

The festival committee planned a busy _____ for the performers.

The judges will _____ one hour for each speaker.

17. **simulate** *(v.)* to imitate

Hang gliders _____ a bird's flight.

18. **submissive** *(adj.)* giving in to the power or control of another

Greta's mean dog becomes a _____ dog when she yells at him.

19. **veil** *(v.)* to cover or hide *(n.)* something that screens or hides

The artist wants to _____ the painting until the gallery opening.

The groom lifted the bride's _____ and kissed her.

20. **writhe** *(v.)* 1. to squirm; 2. to twist

Snakes slither on the branches and _____ on the ground.

Challenge Words

interrogate *(v.)* to question formally

Detectives will _____ the suspect about the crime.

melancholy *(n.)* a depressed state *(adj.)* sad in spirit

Joy and _____ are very opposite feelings.

That _____ song makes me want to weep.

pervade *(v.)* to become spread out through every part of

Rain will _____ the entire state tonight.

stalemate *(n.)* 1. no winner; 2. a contest that ends in a draw

In a _____ between wrestlers, there is no winner or loser.

transcribe *(v.)* 1. to make a written copy; 2. to record

A secretary will _____ the speech onto paper.

Synonyms

Synonyms are words that have the same or nearly the same meanings.

Part 1 Choose the word from the box that is the synonym for each group of words. Write the word on the line.

evolve	irritable	commence	eavesdrop
glorify	principle	ovation	submissive

1. to overhear, listen in, snoop _____

2. to unfold, expand, emerge _____

3. grumpy, ill-tempered, easily annoyed _____

4. applause, acclaim, cheers

_____

5. passive, obedient, docile

_____

6. to originate, set forth, begin

_____

7. to idolize, exalt, bless

_____

8. a rule, belief, law

_____

Part 2 Replace the underlined word(s) with a word from the Basic Words list that means the same or almost the same thing. Write your answer on the line.

9. These candy worms <u>wiggle</u> just like real worms. _____

10. Joey wants to go on the ride that claims to <u>mimic</u> a trip to the moon.

_____

11. The airline pilot announced our cruising speed and <u>height</u> above sea level.

_____

12. If you wish to see the doctor, you must have the secretary check his <u>calendar</u>.

_____

13. Who could have guessed that Michael would <u>retire</u> from basketball to play

baseball? _____

14. Some air fresheners only <u>mask</u> unpleasant odors, not eliminate them.

_____

15. If you <u>squeeze together</u> the aluminum cans, you can get more into the recycle box.

_____

Antonyms

Antonyms are words that have opposite or nearly opposite meanings.

Part 1 Choose the word from the box that is the antonym for each group of words. Write the word on the line.

writhe	resign	submissive	compact

1. to take a job; to keep working _____

2. to rest, be at ease, move easily _____

3. loose, slack; to expand, draw apart _____

4. active, resistant, willful _____

Part 2 Replace the underlined word(s) with a word from the Basic Words list that means the opposite or almost the opposite thing. Write your answer on the line.

5. Grandmother remarked that Kyle had rather <u>pleasant</u> behavior at the dinner table.

_____

6. This is the point where the road rally will <u>end</u>. _____

7. The media is wrong to <u>condemn</u> the celebrity who has broken the law.

_____

8. When the curtain lifts, the careful stage lighting will <u>reveal</u> the performers.

_____

Word Study/Analogies

To complete the following analogies, decide what kind of relationship is shown by the first pair of words. Then fill in the oval next to the pair of words that shows the same relationship.

1. **stove** is to **cook** as **car** is to _____
   - **a.** speed
   - **b.** ride
   - **c.** wash
   - **d.** bicycle

2. **enter** is to **door** as **climb** is to _____
   - **a.** tired
   - **b.** stairs
   - **c.** height
   - **d.** exit

3. **eavesdrop** is to **listen** as **argue** is to _____
   - **a.** mouth
   - **b.** anger
   - **c.** secret
   - **d.** speak

4. **audience** is to **ovation** as **actor** is to _____
   - **a.** people
   - **b.** theater
   - **c.** performance
   - **d.** costume

5. **veil** is to **cover** as **cry** is to _____
   - **a.** happy
   - **b.** weep
   - **c.** baby
   - **d.** soft

Challenge Writing

A Day on the Job Imagine that in the future, you have become a police detective. On a separate sheet of paper, write a description of a typical day on the job using the Challenge Words below. Be sure to describe your responsibilities and how you feel about your work.

| interrogate | melancholy | pervade | stalemate | transcribe |

Tell the Story

Choose the word from the Basic Words list that best completes each sentence. Write the word on the line. You may use the plural form of nouns and the past tense of verbs if necessary.

Choosing a career to __1__ my life to is difficult. But it's time to __2__ my search for the perfect job. Of course I have certain goals and __3__ that I would live my life by, such as having a career that allows me to serve others. With that in mind, I've thought about becoming a doctor, but I __4__ at the sight of __5__ needles. On the other hand, I could be a medical researcher and study a function of the body, such as the __6__ system. But hospitals make me uncomfortable.

I could be an airline pilot, except that I'm afraid of high __7__ . I could be a(n) __8__ , like my uncle who buys and sells stocks on Wall Street, but I can't even make my allowance last a whole week.

A friend of mine operates a machine that __9__ aluminum at a recycling center, but I don't like the __10__ sound of crunching cans. I've always thought it would be fun to be a travel agent and __11__ vacations for people, but I'd be disappointed and __12__ when I couldn't go, too.

I could be a lion tamer in a circus and turn ferocious beasts into __13__ beasts, but I'm allergic to cats. Perhaps as an international spy, I could __14__ on important conversations. But I don't want to live my life under a(n) __15__ of secrecy, so maybe I should do something more out in the open.

I'd like to be an actor who audiences __16__ and give standing __17__ to after each performance. Just one problem with that—I'm too shy to go onstage.

Maybe I will create computer programs that __18__ environment and city problems, but I would have to learn how to solve them first.

Oh well, I'm still young, so I suppose my talents will __19__ over time. And if I do pick a job that I don't like, I guess I always have an option to __20__ and try something else.

1. _____
2. _____
3. _____
4. _____
5. _____
6. _____
7. _____
8. _____
9. _____
10. _____
11. _____
12. _____
13. _____
14. _____
15. _____
16. _____
17. _____
18. _____
19. _____
20. _____

Fun with Words

Your airplane has made an emergency landing on a faraway mountaintop. It will take three days for the rescue team to reach you. You have decided to record your thoughts and activities in a journal. You can write about just one, any two, or all three days of your adventure. However, to make writing in the journal more challenging, you must use at least eight of the chapter vocabulary words.

Chapter 14

Word List

Read each word using the pronunciation key.

Basic Words

ambiguous (am big´ yōō əs)
bulky (bul´ kē)
conceal (kən sēl´)
defect (dē´ fekt)
dignified (dig´ nə fīd
elegance (el´ ə gəns´)
expedition (ek spə dish´ ən)
gnaw (nô)
identity (ī den´ ti tē)
integrate (in´ ti grāt)
meteoric (mēt ē ôr´ ik)
nautical (nôt´ i kəl)
negligent (neg´ li jənt)
nullify (nul´ ə fī)
pacifist (pas´ ə fist)
profit (prof´ it)
retaliate (ri tal´ ē āt)
scenic (sēn´ ik)
swindle (swin´ dəl)
velocity (və los´ ə tē)

Challenge Words

enchant (en chant´)
inflict (in flikt´)
lax (laks)
quaint (kwānt)
stifle (stī´ fəl)

Word Study

Prefixes

The prefixes *il-*, *im-*, *in-*, and *ir-* are forms of the prefix *in-*, which means *not* or *in, into, within.*

illegal (i lē´ gəl) *(adj.)* not legal
immeasurable (i mezh´ ər ə bəl) *(adj.)* too vast to be measured
immigrant (im´ ə grənt) *(n.)* a person who comes into a country to settle
incomplete (in kəm plēt´) *(adj.)* not complete
independent (in di pen´ dənt) *(adj.)* getting no help from others
irreversible (ir i vers´ ə bəl) *(adj.)* not able to be changed

Be Careful!

Commonly Misspelled Words

casserole	eighth	foreign
height	leisure	seize

# Words in Context

Read each sentence below to decipher the meaning of each boldface word. Use reasoning skills and the remainder of the sentence to help you. Write the meaning of the word on the line.

1. You must **conceal** Karen's birthday gift before she arrives so it will be a surprise.

_____

2. It's too difficult for you to carry that **bulky** box by yourself.

_____

3. The First Lady's gown for the inaugural ball gave her a look of **elegance.**

_____

4. My teacher will **integrate** the study of literature with the study of history.

_____

5. After six months, our restaurant made enough **profit** to allow us to expand.

_____

6. My brother wears a white **nautical** uniform since he joined the U.S. Coast Guard.

_____

7. The tour bus driver thought we would enjoy the **scenic** drive to the beach.

_____

8. There is a stately and **dignified** painting of the senator hanging in the state capitol.

_____

9. An honest comic book salesman would not **swindle** a serious collector.

_____

10. During the storm, the wind **velocity** reached 80 miles per hour.

_____

Word Meanings

Within each group, study the spelling, part(s) of speech, and meaning(s) of each word. Complete each sentence by writing the word on the line. Then read the sentence.

Basic Words

1. **ambiguous** *(adj.)* 1. unclear; 2. uncertain; 3. having more than one meaning

   Maybe is an _____ answer to my request to go to the movies.

2. **bulky** *(adj.)* 1. clumsy; 2. massive; 3. large

   The deliveryman stumbled up the stairs carrying _____ packages.

3. **conceal** *(v.)* to hide or keep out of sight

   The jeweler will _____ the jewels each night in a secret drawer.

4. **defect** *(n.)* 1. a flaw; 2. weakness; 3. imperfection

   The new stereo wouldn't work because of a _____ in the system.

5. **dignified** *(adj.)* 1. showing or expressing the quality of being worthy or honored; 2. having dignity; 3. noble; 4. serious

   The _____ Southern gentleman escorted the lady to the opera.

6. **elegance** *(n.)* 1. good taste; 2. distinction

   The prince lived in a palace surrounded by _____ and beauty.

7. **expedition** *(n.)* a journey undertaken for a specific purpose

   The purpose of the _____ to the moon was to study rocks.

8. **gnaw** *(v.)* 1. to eat or chew at; 2. to erode or wear away

   A gerbil can _____ its way out of a cardboard box.

9. **identity** *(n.)* 1. individuality, uniqueness; 2. what or who a person or thing is

   A wolf in sheep's clothing is disguising its _____ .

10. **integrate** *(v.)* 1. to bring together; 2. to blend into a whole

    The new plan will _____ fifth grade into the middle school.

11. **meteoric** *(adj.)* 1. of or like a mass of stone or metal that comes toward Earth from outer space; 2. happening fast or suddenly

After just one hit song, the singer had a _____ rise to stardom.

12. **nautical** *(adj.)* having to do with sailors, ships, or navigation

Colorful _____ flags fly from the boats.

13. **negligent** *(adj.)* indifferent, careless

To improve his grades, Roy will need to improve his _____ attitude.

14. **nullify** *(v.)* 1. to put an end to; 2. to make of no value; 3. to invalidate

An outbreak of war will _____ the peace treaty.

15. **pacifist** *(adj.)* of or relating to the opposition of war or violence *(n.)* one who opposes war or violence

The group, Fathers Against Violence, organized a _____ protest.

Shanti went to India to live the life of a peace-loving _____ .

16. **profit** *(n.)* 1. the earnings from a business; 2. a gain; 3. benefit *(v.)* to create a gain from a business

Our school store hopes to make a _____ on the sale of pencils.

The Boosters' Club will _____ from a successful magazine sale.

17. **retaliate** *(v.)* to return or pay back a wrong, especially to get revenge

Darnell might _____ for your trick with a joke of his own.

18. **scenic** *(adj.)* having an attractive or pleasing landscape

The _____ park along the Hudson River is a lovely picnic spot.

19. **swindle** *(v.)* 1. to cheat; 2. to trick *(n.)* a fraud or cheating act

The ticket scalper's aim was to _____ the unsuspecting tourists.

Unfortunately, the phony charity _____ fooled many people.

20. **velocity** *(n.)* 1. quickness; 2. rate of speed

The motorcycle sped past us with dangerous _____ .

Challenge Words

enchant *(v.)* to deeply attract or rouse to great admiration

This song will _____ and fascinate you.

inflict *(v.)* 1. to give by striking; 2. to cause to be endured

You must not _____ pain on other people.

lax *(adj.)* 1. not tense, loose, relaxed; 2. careless; 3. not strict enough

A _____ father should be more strict with his child.

quaint *(adj.)* unusual in an amusing or interesting way

"Hickory, Dickory, Dock" is a _____ little rhyme.

stifle *(v.)* 1. to smother or suffocate; 2. to hold back

Please _____ your sneezes with this handkerchief.

Synonyms

Synonyms are words that have the same or nearly the same meanings.

Part 1 Choose the word from the box that is the synonym for each group of words. Write the word on the line.

velocity	conceal	defect	ambiguous
pacifist	bulky	retaliate	swindle

1. speed, quickness, swiftness _____

2. to deceive; a trick _____

3. a failing, drawback _____

4. vague, indefinite, obscure _____

5. big, awkward _____

6. to screen, hide, cover _____

7. to get revenge, repay, return _____

8. peaceful; one who is antiwar _____

Part 2 Replace the underlined word(s) with a word from the Basic Words list that means the same or almost the same thing. Write your answer on the line.

9. The <u>proceeds</u> from the cookie sale will help pay for a trip to Mystic, Connecticut.

_____

10. The salesperson showed us party dresses with grace and <u>style</u>. _____

11. An Antarctica <u>voyage</u> is for the brave and hardy. _____

12. A loss to their rival school will <u>stop</u> the team's chances for a championship.

_____

13. The rats are kept in wire cages so that they do not <u>bite</u> their way out.

_____

14. Ralph pays library fines because of his <u>neglectful</u> habit of returning books late.

_____

15. I like the way our team of teachers <u>combine</u> language arts and writing.

_____

Antonyms

Antonyms are words that have opposite or nearly opposite meanings.

Part 1 Choose the word from the box that is the antonym for each group of words. Write the word on the line.

retaliate	nautical	negligent	scenic	defect

1. a strength, perfection, virtue _____

2. to ignore, turn the other cheek _____

3. careful, exact, mindful   _____

4. having to do with land   _____

5. not pleasing, unattractive   _____

Part 2 Replace the underlined word(s) with a word from the Basic Words list that means the opposite or almost the opposite thing. Write your answer on the line.

6. The students asked the principal to <u>separate</u> the boys' and girls' gym classes.

   _____

7. The truck driver washed her truck with amazing <u>roughness</u>. _____

8. A <u>small</u> load of laundry causes the washing machine to make a terrible noise.

   _____

9. The general expected to receive a <u>definite</u> answer from headquarters.

   _____

10. Will the witness choose to <u>reveal</u> the true identity of the murderer?

   _____

Word Study/Prefixes

Choose the word from the box that best completes each of the following sentences. Write the word in the blank. You may use the plural form of nouns or the past tense of verbs if necessary.

illegal	immeasurable	immigrant
incomplete	independent	irreversible

1. Did you know that it's _____ to jaywalk across the street?

2. The damage was _____ , so they tore the building down.

3. Audrey's dishes don't match because she has an _____ set.

4. Elsie was grateful for everyone's _____ kindness.

5. My ancestors came to this country as _____ from Ireland.

6. You'll be _____ when you have an apartment of your own.

Tell the Story

Choose the word from the Basic Words list that best completes each sentence. Write the word on the line. You may use the plural form of nouns and the past tense of verbs if necessary.

President Jefferson believed the United States would __1__ from greater knowledge of the West. He asked two explorers, Meriwether Lewis and William Clark, to lead a(n) __2__ from Missouri to Washington in the early 1800s. The explorers were instructed to undertake the journey as __3__ . They were to promote peace with the Native Americans.

The men could not afford to be __4__ planners. Everything they would need had to be carried with them. __5__ items could not be taken on the journey. The __6__ of the Missouri River determined how far and how fast the boats could travel each day. Several men in the party had __7__ skills that proved useful on uncharted rivers.

Many of the men had __8__ feelings about meeting Native Americans for the first time. They had heard tales of Native Americans who tried to __9__ newcomers out of their horses. Some were afraid that the Native Americans would __10__ for problems caused by earlier explorers. Lewis and Clark asked a woman named Sacajawea to travel with them to explain their __11__ to the Native Americans. The explorers met a Mandan tribal leader who wore a headdress of great __12__ . The man's leadership and __13__ manner were impressive.

Lewis and Clark wrote about the beautiful, __14__ surroundings, camping on the plains, and seeing __15__ rocks, often called shooting stars, falling across the sky. They were amazed by the prairie dogs that __16__ themselves in burrows. They were not pleased when the prairie dogs __17__ through bags of supplies.

Sometimes a boat would develop a(n) __18__ , forcing them to stop and make repairs, or they would come upon the great waterfalls of the Missouri River. None of this could __19__ their eagerness to reach the Pacific Ocean and help to __20__ the eastern and western parts of our country.

1. _____

2. _____

3. _____

4. _____

5. _____

6. _____

7. _____

8. _____

9. _____

10. _____

11. _____

12. _____

13. _____

14. _____

15. _____

16. _____

17. _____

18. _____

19. _____

20. _____

Challenge Writing

A New Land Imagine that you are an explorer who has discovered a new land. Write a journal entry about your discovery, using the Challenge Words below. Be sure to describe the people and the landscape.

enchant	inflict	lax	quaint	stifle

_____

_____

_____

_____

_____

_____

_____

_____

_____

_____

_____

_____

_____

_____

Fun with Words

How carefully did you read the story on page 164? Write the vocabulary word that goes with each definition. Then unscramble the letters in the circles to form two words that tell what Lewis and Clark were trying to reach.

1. to hide

◯ _ _ ◯ _ _ _

2. to pay back a wrong

_ _ _ ◯ _ ◯ _ _ _

3. of or like a stone that falls from space to earth

_ ◯ _ _ _ _ _ ◯

4. unclear

◯ _ _ _ _ _ _ _ _

5. the earnings from a business

◯ _ _ _ _ _

6. to put an end to

◯ _ _ _ _ ◯ _

7. to bring together

◯ _ _ _ _ _ _ _

8. a journey for a specific purpose

_ _ _ _ _ _ _ ◯ _

Answer: THE _____

Word List

Read each word using the pronunciation key.

Basic Words

analyze (an´ ə līz)
bulletin (boŏl´ i tən)
confidential (kon fə den´ shəl)
delegate (*n.* del´ ə gət)(*v.* del´ ə gāt)
dignity (dig´ nə tē)
element (el´ ə mənt)
extraordinary (ek strôr´ də nâr ē)
gradual (gra´ joō wəl)
ignite (ig nīt´)
ingenious (in jēn´ yəs)
jovial (jō´ vē əl)
miniature (mi´ nē ə choŏr)
neutral (noō´ trəl)
parcel (pär´ səl)
puncture (puŋk´ chər)
retreat (ri trēt´)
slander (slan´ dər)
technical (tek´ ni kəl)
tendency (ten´ dən sē)
verge (vərj)

Challenge Words

lame (lām)
malady (mal´ ə dē)
malignant (mə lig´ nənt)
unique (yoō nēk´)
vengeance (ven´ jəns)

Word Study

Root Words

The Latin root *capere* means *take*.
A root often changes its form, and *cap*, *cept*, and *ceipt* are forms of *capere*.

accept (ak sept´) *(v.)* to willingly take or receive
capacity (kə pas´ ə tē) *(n.)* the largest amount that can be held
capture (kap´ chər) *(v.)* to take by force
receipt (ri sēt´) *(n.)* a written statement that something has been received
receive (ri sēv´) *(v.)* to take into one's possession
reception (ri sep´ shən) *(n.)* a gathering to receive and welcome people

Be Careful!

Commonly Misspelled Words

| chief | fountain | mischievous |
| relief | relieve | yield |

# Words in Context

Read each sentence below to decipher the meaning of each boldface word. Use reasoning skills and the remainder of the sentence to help you. Write the meaning of the word on the line.

1. The admiral's widow stood with **dignity** while the band played the Navy hymn.

    _____

2. Lightning can **ignite** a tree and begin a forest fire.

    _____

3. I have a **tendency** to talk a lot when I get nervous.

    _____

4. After several years of **gradual** growth, Jason shot up four inches over the summer.

    _____

5. Will you mail this **parcel** of newspaper clippings to Aunt Mary?

    _____

6. The class chose to send Carmen as our **delegate** to the convention.

    _____

7. A nail will **puncture** a tire and cause it to flatten.

    _____

8. I always laugh in Mr. Chapa's class because he has a **jovial** personality.

    _____

9. The Swiss took a **neutral** position during the war and stayed out of the conflict.

    _____

10. I haven't made up my mind yet, but I am on the **verge** of looking for a job.

    _____

Word Meanings

Within each group, study the spelling, part(s) of speech, and meaning(s) of each word. Complete each sentence by writing the word on the line. Then read the sentence.

Basic Words

1. **analyze** *(v.)* 1. to divide something into parts; 2. to examine thoroughly and in detail

   The doctor will first _____ the data, then make his diagnosis.

2. **bulletin** *(n.)* a brief statement of information or news

   The weather emergency _____ flashed on the TV screen.

3. **confidential** *(adj.)* 1. relayed as a secret; 2. private

   The accountant keeps _____ reports in a locked cabinet.

4. **delegate** *(n.)* 1. a person with the authority to act for others; 2. a representative *(v.)* to choose a person as a representative

   As our _____ to the convention, Mrs. Cohn will cast our vote.

   The teacher will _____ students to do the classroom tasks.

5. **dignity** *(n.)* the condition of being worthy, honored, and respected

   The Egyptian president's funeral was conducted with great _____ .

6. **element** *(n.)* 1. one of more than one hundred basic substances from which all things are made; 2. a simple part

   Gold is an _____ with great value.

7. **extraordinary** *(adj.)* 1. unusual; 2. remarkable; 3. uncommon

   Thomas Jefferson had an _____ , inventive mind.

8. **gradual** *(adj.)* 1. happening in small degrees or steps; 2. little by little

   Regular, _____ savings is better than not saving money at all.

9. **ignite** *(v.)* 1. to set on fire; 2. to begin to burn

   _____ the kindling first when you build a fire in the fireplace.

10. **ingenious** *(adj.)* 1. inventive; 2. clever

   Earl amazed his boss with his _____ , time-saving invention.

11. **jovial** *(adj.)* 1. good-humored; 2. full of fun; 3. merry

Our family reunions are great fun due to our _____ Uncle Frank.

12. **miniature** *(adj.)* created or made on a very tiny scale

Even today, a _____ Statue of Liberty is a prized souvenir.

13. **neutral** *(adj.)* 1. not taking either side in a dispute; 2. uninvolved

The _____ countries will not support either warring nation.

14. **parcel** *(n.)* a wrapped package

I need string and paper to wrap the _____ before mailing it.

15. **puncture** *(n.)* a hole that is created by something pointed or sharp *(v.)* to create a hole with something pointed or sharp

Joe got the _____ patched and put the tire back on the car.

The object of the game was to _____ the balloon with a dart.

16. **retreat** *(v.)* 1. to go or move back; 2. to withdraw from something *(n.)* the act of moving back or withdrawing

To save themselves, the residents will _____ from the high water.

The beekeeper made a hasty _____ from the overturned beehive.

17. **slander** *(v.)* to talk falsely or incorrectly about someone *(n.)* a false or incorrect statement meant to harm another person's reputation

Newspapers behave irresponsibly when they _____ celebrities.

The radio broadcasts spread _____ about the enemy.

18. **technical** *(adj.)* having to do with a mechanical or scientific subject

Carol, a _____ writer, writes computer manuals.

19. **tendency** *(n.)* a habit of acting or thinking a certain way

Mom has a _____ to worry about me, but I'm glad she does.

20. **verge** *(n.)* 1. the point that something happens or begins; 2. the brink

The year 2000 is the _____ of a new century and a new millennium.

Challenge Words

lame *(adj.)* physically disabled or weak

The _____ horse had trouble walking.

malady *(n.)* a disease or disorder

What _____ made you so sick?

malignant *(adj.)* tending to produce death, destruction, or deterioration

_____ wounds were a cause of death in the Civil War.

unique *(adj.)* 1. being the only one; 2. unusual

This _____ , one-of-a-kind watch is not for sale.

vengeance *(n.)* punishment in retaliation for an offense

I seek _____ for the wrongs you have done to me.

Synonyms

Synonyms are words that have the same or nearly the same meanings.

Part 1 Choose the word from the box that is the synonym for each group of words. Write the word on the line.

retreat	tendency	parcel	ignite
verge	neutral	ingenious	miniature

1. an edge, limit, boundary _____

2. a leaning, bent, likelihood _____

3. to fall back, move away from _____

4. a bundle, packet, package _____

5. standing by, inactive, unconcerned _____

6. little, small, tiny _____

7. to light, burst into flames, burn   _____

8. bright, keen, intelligent   _____

Part 2 Replace the underlined word(s) with a word from the Basic Words list that means the same or almost the same thing. Write your answer on the line.

9. A friendly, <u>jolly</u> greeter welcomes shoppers at the store's entrance.

_____

10. The trucks on the highway made only <u>slow</u> progress in the blizzard.

_____

11. The police will carefully <u>study</u> the hostage situation before taking action.

_____

12. The public address system crackled and then we heard the morning

<u>announcement</u>. _____

13. Liz keeps her diary locked because it is <u>personal</u>. _____

14. The conductor directed the band to play "Hail to the Chief" with <u>honor</u>.

_____

15. Niagara Falls is an <u>incredible</u> sight. _____

Antonyms

Antonyms are words that have opposite or nearly opposite meanings.

Part 1 Choose the word from the box that is the antonym for each group of words. Write the word on the line.

extraordinary	neutral	gradual	confidential	ignite

1. known to all, public   _____

2. involved, taking an active part   _____

3. sudden, hasty, all at once _____

4. usual, normal, ordinary _____

5. to extinguish, put out, quench _____

Part 2 Replace the underlined word(s) with a word from the Basic Words list that means the opposite or almost the opposite thing. Write your answer on the line.

6. Bunk beds in my room are an <u>inept</u> solution to make more space.

_____

7. With Aunt Sadie visiting, we have many <u>cheerless</u> dinners. _____

8. We have <u>full-sized</u> horses in the barn. _____

9. Readers should know that the unauthorized biography is full of <u>truth</u>.

_____

10. At the height of battle, General Lee ordered his troops to <u>advance</u>.

_____

 # **Word Study/**Root Words

The word meanings in the circles come from the Latin root *capere.* The word meanings are different, but all are related to the meaning "take." Complete the word web with these *capere* words.

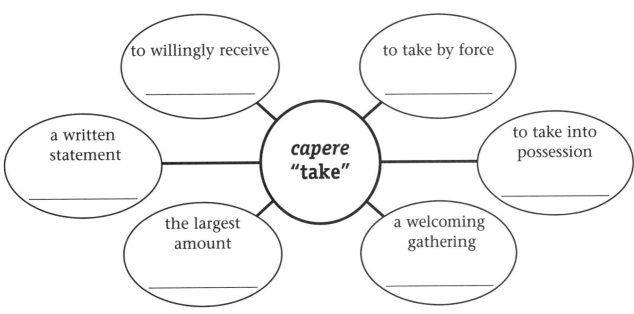

Tell the Story

Choose the word from the Basic Words list that best completes each sentence. Write the word on the line. You may use the plural form of nouns and the past tense of verbs if necessary.

The personal computer is one of the most important __1__ advances of the century. Its __2__ design makes computers user-friendly. This is the chief reason for the personal computer's __3__ popularity. One important __4__ of the computer's inner workings is the microchip. Because the __5__ microchip is small in size but big in capability, it helped to __6__ a computer revolution that spread like wildfire.

My teacher, a very __7__ person, wants my class to have fun as we apply our computer knowledge to something interesting. So we are using a computer to __8__ the cost and effectiveness of a variety of headache medicines. We're also investigating the advertising of competitive medications to determine whether the ads are __9__ or truth. We are trying to take a(n) __10__ position in our analysis and not recommend one medication over another. As a result of this study, I have been asked to be a(n) __11__ to the computer fair, where I will present our results and represent our school with honor and __12__ .

When I'm at home I sometimes __13__ to my room to play games on my computer. I can keep all my game scores private by assigning a(n) __14__ password to the computer program. But my parents say I have a(n) __15__ to spend too much time on the computer and not enough time on my home-work. They are not trying to __16__ my dreams of being a computer wizard, but are concerned that I might neglect other subjects.

Until last week, I was on the __17__ of buying a more powerful computer with the money I've been saving. I had been reading __18__ on the Internet to keep track of the new computers and their prices. Then a surprise __19__ came in the mail. It was my uncle's old computer, which is much more powerful than mine. I've been taking a(n) __20__ approach to learning all it can do.

1. _____
2. _____
3. _____
4. _____
5. _____
6. _____
7. _____
8. _____
9. _____
10. _____
11. _____
12. _____
13. _____
14. _____
15. _____
16. _____
17. _____
18. _____
19. _____
20. _____

Challenge Writing

The Cure You have created a medicine to cure a disease. Write directions on how to make this medicine, using the Challenge Words below. Be sure to describe the ingredients and how you put them together.

lame	malady	malignant	unique	vengeance

Fun with Words

Unscramble the vocabulary words. Then write the letter of the definition that matches each unscrambled word.

1. greev _____ _____ a. a package

2. teagleed _____ _____ b. uninvolved

3. drensal _____ _____ c. private information

4. tieing _____ _____ d. to make a hole

5. cendenyt _____ _____ e. inventive

6. laudarg _____ _____ f. unusual

7. eniousing _____ _____ g. the beginning point

8. denfinoctial _____ _____ h. about a scientific subject

9. menteel _____ _____ i. to set on fire

10. lautner _____ _____ j. a brief statement of news

11. tublenil _____ _____ k. to talk falsely about

12. draniroartexy _____ _____ l. happening little by little

13. chentacil _____ _____ m. a simple part

14. renupcut _____ _____ n. a representative

15. crelap _____ _____ o. a habit

Review 13-15

Word Meanings Underline the word that is best defined by each phrase.

1. loud and long applause
   a. elegance   **b.** ovation   **c.** dignity   **d.** puncture

2. height above the ground
   a. altitude   **b.** identity   **c.** ambiguous   **d.** expedition

3. speed of something
   a. delegate   **b.** element   **c.** broker   **d.** velocity

4. not careful
   a. nautical   **b.** scenic   **c.** negligent   **d.** compact

5. to go backward
   a. retreat   **b.** eavesdrop   **c.** gnaw   **d.** altitude

6. a basic law
   a. pacifist   **b.** puncture   **c.** principle   **d.** profit

7. to put out of sight
   a. conceal   **b.** ignite   **c.** dedicate   **d.** retaliate

8. fun-loving and jolly
   a. submissive   **b.** jovial   **c.** meteoric   **d.** extraordinary

9. very small
   a. ambiguous   **b.** miniature   **c.** submissive   **d.** dignified

10. to quit or retire
    a. schedule   **b.** simulate   **c.** swindle   **d.** resign

11. an imperfect part
    a. defect   **b.** velocity   **c.** slander   **d.** principle

12. so big as to be awkward
    a. bulky   **b.** hypodermic   **c.** confidential   **d.** ingenious

13. to begin
    a. evolve   **b.** commence   **c.** glorify   **d.** integrate

14. joining neither side in a war
    a. irritable   **b.** gradual   **c.** technical   **d.** neutral

15. to study the parts of something
    a. writhe   **b.** nullify   **c.** analyze   **d.** slander

16. a necessary or basic part
    a. broker   **b.** element   **c.** veil   **d.** verge

17. noble and proper
    a. jovial   **b.** digestive   **c.** nautical   **d.** dignified

18. to do harm in return for harm done
    a. evolve   **b.** retaliate   **c.** resign   **d.** eavesdrop

19. something that covers or hides
    a. parcel   **b.** bulletin   **c.** profit   **d.** veil

20. relating to science
    a. meteoric   **b.** metallic   **c.** technical   **d.** hypodermic

Sentence Completion Choose the word from the box that best completes each of the following sentences. Write the word in the blank.

integrated	tendency	expedition	digestive	simulate
bulletin	extraordinary	scheduled	identity	gnawed

1. In the stomach, _____ juices break down food.

2. The squirrel _____ a hole in the telephone wire.

3. My cousin was asked to demonstrate her _____ juggling skills.

4. Ana and Thomas are planning a(n) _____ to South America.

5. The latest weather _____ said a thunderstorm is approaching.

6. In drama class we were asked to _____ an elephant walking.

7. Peter did not reveal his _____ until the end of the costume party.

8. Have you _____ a meeting with the principal?

9. I have a(n) _____ to ignore my alarm clock in the morning.

10. The band director _____ the sounds of all the instruments into a pleasing melody.

Fill in the Blanks Underline the pair of words that best completes each sentence.

1. A person who would _____ may be a person without high _____ .
   a. eavesdrop, principles   **c.** swindle, ovations
   b. conceal, bulletins   **d.** resign, parcels

2. The convention _____ attended a(n) _____ meeting.

   a. expedition, gradual   **c.** delegates, confidential

   b. pacifists, miniature   **d.** brokers, metallic

3. The company president is _____ and friendly, but she has _____, too.

   a. jovial, dignity   **c.** irritable, elegance

   b. neutral, velocity   **d.** negligent, schedules

4. The scientists _____ the meteor fragments and reported that they were _____.

   a. integrated, submissive   **c.** concealed, irritable

   b. ignited, technical   **d.** analyzed, metallic

5. According to the _____, the game will _____ at exactly 7:05.

   a. slander, swindle   **c.** altitude, nullify

   b. schedule, commence   **d.** velocity, retaliate

6. The amusement park ride _____ a(n) _____ to the North Pole.

   a. punctures, hypodermic   **c.** simulates, expedition

   b. identifies, tendency   **d.** evolves, miniature

7. The package is _____ but it contains a(n) _____ surprise.

   a. bulky, extraordinary   **c.** scenic, nautical

   b. compact, submissive   **d.** ambiguous, neutral

8. The author _____ his book to his _____ schnauzer.

   a. nullified, negligent   **c.** integrated, confidential

   b. gnawed, jovial   **d.** dedicated, miniature

9. The _____ hopes his new business will begin to show a(n) _____ quickly.

   a. bulletin, defect   **c.** puncture, dignity

   b. delegate, element   **d.** broker, profit

10. The mountain climbers were on the _____ of reaching the peak when a snowstorm forced them to _____ .

   a. verge, retreat   **c.** velocity, profit

   b. altitude, swindle   **d.** elegance, defect

Classifying Words

Sort the words in the box by writing each word to complete a phrase in the correct category.

altitude	bulletin	commence	concealed	dedicates
defects	expedition	extraordinary	identify	jovial
meteoric	negligent	ovation	pacifist	parcels
schedule	submissive	swindled	technical	velocity

Words You Might Use to Talk about Personalities

1. a main character that is careless and _____

2. a professor who _____ her life to her job

3. a former soldier who is now a _____

4. a grandfather who is always kind and _____

5. a well-trained dog that is _____ to her owner

Words You Might Use to Talk about Airplane Trips

6. checking the _____ to see if your flight is on time

7. flying at an _____ of 35,000 feet

8. the co-pilot's _____ knowledge

9. flight attendants stowing _____ in the overhead bins

10. no _____ in the landing gear

Words You Might Use to Talk about the Weather

11. a special _____ about the hurricane

12. a _____ rise in temperature in just one hour

13. an _____ winter warm spell

14. a late snowfall that _____ blooming plants

15. high _____ winds that knocked down power lines

Words You Might Use to Talk about the News

16. a stock broker who _____ innocent customers

17. a new space program that is about to _____

18. a music star who gets a standing _____ at her concert

19. a witness who is able to _____ the robbery suspect

20. the latest report about the _____ to Antarctica

Posttest

Choosing the Definitions
Fill in the oval next to the item that best defines the boldfaced word in each sentence.

1. Grandma's smile is as welcoming as a **beacon** in the night.
   - (a.) snack
   - (b.) light
   - (c.) yell
   - (d.) dream

2. From an early age, Leatha knew her **vocation** was to be a doctor.
   - (a.) schedule
   - (b.) free time
   - (c.) career
   - (d.) specialty

3. Since they bought their trailer, Grandma and Grandpa are **nomads** every winter.
   - (a.) wanderers
   - (b.) elderly
   - (c.) campers
   - (d.) homeless

4. The speaker chose not to **acknowledge** the other candidate's presence.
   - (a.) ignore
   - (b.) sense
   - (c.) give back
   - (d.) recognize

5. Tisha loves to snuggle inside her **bulky** overcoat on snowy winter days.
   - (a.) colorful
   - (b.) large
   - (c.) warm
   - (d.) old

6. The process for solving the math problem was **incomprehensible** to Mark.
   - (a.) easy
   - (b.) understandable
   - (c.) unclear
   - (d.) known

7. The members of the party have a **pacifist** agenda.
   - (a.) childish
   - (b.) rowdy
   - (c.) effective
   - (d.) anti-war

8. No matter how hard she tried, Charise could not **puncture** the balloon.
   - (a.) pop
   - (b.) hang
   - (c.) blow up
   - (d.) fill

9. The tree lost several **boughs** in the storm.
   - (a.) leaves
   - (b.) bark
   - (c.) branches
   - (d.) trunks

10. Erik was willing to **grovel** before the judge to get his fine reduced.
    - (a.) speak softly
    - (b.) humble oneself
    - (c.) walk proudly
    - (d.) quiver

11. The plane was flying at a dangerous **altitude**.
    - (a.) angle
    - (b.) speed
    - (c.) height
    - (d.) temperature

12. Because of the **drought**, the corn crop was sparse.
    - (a.) late
    - (b.) green
    - (c.) dead
    - (d.) thin

13. The ingenious invention has a **dual** purpose.
    - (a.) double
    - (b.) boring
    - (c.) noble
    - (d.) unusual

14. The neighbors joined together to clean up the **urban** playground.
    - (a.) dirty
    - (b.) rural
    - (c.) school
    - (d.) city

15. The architect planned an **annex** for the old school building.
    - (a.) playground
    - (b.) expansion
    - (c.) shed
    - (d.) landscape

16. The president wrote a **dignified** response to the child's letter.
    a. angry   b. slow   c. bold   d. serious

17. I saw the rescue workers **weaving** through the crowd.
    a. jogging   b. twisting   c. crying   d. skipping

18. The flood waters **engulfed** the small island.
    a. floated   b. went around   c. submerged   d. moistened

19. We gasped as we watched the **aerial** stunt.
    a. risky   b. on the ground c. in the air   d. successful

20. The builders didn't see the **defect** in the plan until they tried to carry it out.
    a. weakness   b. surprise   c. detail   d. change

21. The city council will **debate** the new law at tonight's meeting.
    a. pass   b. overturn   c. write   d. discuss

22. I wonder how Jason will **react** to the bad news.
    a. ignore   b. hurry   c. respond   d. deny

23. The diplomats struggled to build good **relations** between the two nations.
    a. connections   b. health   c. records   d. moods

24. The boys thought it was fun to **collaborate** on the song.
    a. learn to play b. make fun of   c. listen to   d. work together

25. Everyone worked hard to make the **division** of the bake sale money fair.
    a. spending   b. sharing   c. saving   d. counting

26. The nurse says Maria will recover from the **ailment** quickly.
    a. shock   b. illness   c. journey   d. operation

27. Arnie was proud when the dentist said he didn't have even one **cavity**.
    a. crooked tooth b. filling   c. hole in a tooth d. tantrum

28. The leaders hoped to be able to **integrate** the groups from the two different schools smoothly.
    a. compare   b. study   c. talk to   d. combine

29. My new baby brother is cute when he is not being **irritable**.
    a. grumpy   b. calm   c. sweet   d. sleeping

30. Ellie was carrying so many **parcels** she was afraid she would drop one.
    a. umbrellas   b. packages   c. kittens   d. books

Word Relations
Synonyms are words that have the same or nearly the same meanings. Antonyms are words that have the opposite or nearly the opposite meanings.

In the blank before each pair of words, write S if the words are synonyms, A if they are antonyms, or N if they are not related.

1. _____ nullify   associate
2. _____ reveal   veil
3. _____ glorify   slander
4. _____ hypodermic   absorb
5. _____ stir   invigorate
6. _____ ignite   quench
7. _____ duplicate   simulate
8. _____ civilize   signify
9. _____ acute   keen
10. _____ serene   frantic
11. _____ oracle   ointment
12. _____ whisk   hustle
13. _____ manipulate   coax
14. _____ inevitable   dissolve
15. _____ besiege   bombard

16. _____ illicit   enlist
17. _____ digestion   prevention
18. _____ compact   vast
19. _____ deter   impede
20. _____ retaliate   negotiate
21. _____ ingenious   extraordinary
22. _____ literal   figurative
23. _____ slogan   debate
24. _____ mental   physical
25. _____ fierce   savage
26. _____ trifle   tedious
27. _____ ambiguous   incomprehensible
28. _____ discontent   contentment
29. _____ scholar   scoundrel
30. _____ nobility   dignity

Using Context Clues
Fill in the oval next to the phrase that best completes each sentence.

1. If you travel to an **exotic** land, you will go
   - a. across the river.
   - b. over a mountain.
   - c. to your neighbor's house.
   - d. to a foreign country.

2. Sam felt like a **hypocrite** when he
   - a. missed the last bus.
   - b. said his name was Mike.
   - c. sang out of tune.
   - d. rescued the stranded kitten.

3. When she saw the restaurant's **elegance**, Martha exclaimed,
   - **a.** "Can we go somewhere else?"
   - **b.** "I'd like some dessert."
   - **c.** "What good taste the owners have!"
   - **d.** "What an ugly place!"

4. An **angle** can always be found in
   - **a.** a toolbox.
   - **b.** an automobile tire.
   - **c.** a globe.
   - **d.** a baseball diamond.

5. If your **digestive** system isn't working properly, you
   - **a.** may have a stomach ache.
   - **b.** may have trouble breathing.
   - **c.** should get help from a gardener.
   - **d.** should get help from a banker.

6. Kara avoided **strenuous** activity after
   - **a.** the stove broke.
   - **b.** she hurt her back.
   - **c.** her parents returned.
   - **d.** she learned to swim.

7. If a crowd **erupts** after a concert, it
   - **a.** leaves quietly.
   - **b.** goes backstage.
   - **c.** cheers and claps loudly.
   - **d.** sits back down.

8. When Jerod saw Katie **sneer**, he knew she
   - **a.** wanted to eat lunch.
   - **b.** was very excited.
   - **c.** wanted to talk to him.
   - **d.** was still mad at him.

9. A **spectrum** in the sky is
   - **a.** a rainbow.
   - **b.** an airplane.
   - **c.** a shooting star.
   - **d.** a full moon.

10. After Sylvia **resigned** as president of the Spanish Club,
    - **a.** she mailed the letter.
    - **b.** she changed the club's rules.
    - **c.** the club elected a new president.
    - **d.** the club welcomed her with a party.

11. We spent all afternoon digging a **shaft** for
    - **a.** the doghouse.
    - **b.** the new well.
    - **c.** a treehouse.
    - **d.** a driveway.

12. If you feel the ground **vibrate**, you may be
    - **a.** under a bridge.
    - **b.** running too fast.
    - **c.** in a hurricane.
    - **d.** in an earthquake.

13. If someone speaks with **clarity**,
    - **a.** it is difficult to respond.
    - **b.** he is in a hurry
    - **c.** she is easy to understand.
    - **d.** you can't hear the words.

14. To **analyze** the test results you must
    - **a.** study them closely.
    - **b.** take the test yourself.
    - **c.** tell everyone about them.
    - **d.** tell no one about them.

15. The king lost his **dignity** for a moment when he
    - **a.** forgot where he put it.
    - **c.** woke up this morning.
    - **b.** dropped it in the river.
    - **d.** tripped on his robe.

16. When you **presume** that you're invited to a party, you
    - **a.** know for a fact you are invited.
    - **c.** are upset that you are not invited.
    - **b.** assume that you are invited.
    - **d.** aren't sure you are invited.

17. You may sign up for the **"Juvenile Jog"** if you are
    - **a.** an athlete.
    - **c.** under fifteen years old.
    - **b.** a grandparent.
    - **d.** over twenty-five years old.

18. If you have an **obligation** to baby-sit, you
    - **a.** have promised to baby-sit.
    - **c.** are paid to watch small children.
    - **b.** do not enjoy baby-sitting.
    - **d.** baby-sit for free.

19. The doctor looked at Geri's **pupils** after he gave her
    - **a.** braces.
    - **c.** fillings.
    - **b.** bandages.
    - **d.** eye drops.

20. One of his answers was **invalid**, but the others were
    - **a.** wrong.
    - **c.** correct.
    - **b.** sad.
    - **d.** not logical.

21. An animal in **captivity** may
    - **a.** fly away if it wants to
    - **c.** live in a cage.
    - **b.** live in the wild.
    - **d.** control its own life.

22. Something made of **granite** would
    - **a.** feel very hard.
    - **c.** bend in the wind.
    - **b.** be soft as a pillow.
    - **d.** be light as a feather.

23. A person who is **gullible**
    - **a.** keeps birds for a hobby.
    - **c.** believes what you say.
    - **b.** is always in a bad mood.
    - **d.** is very suspicious.

24. If you take the **initiative**, you
    - **a.** are afraid to go first.
    - **c.** may serve time in prison.
    - **b.** may become known as a leader.
    - **d.** are willing to wait a while.

25. A **boisterous** crowd
    - **a.** is quiet and sad.
    - **c.** is marching in rows.
    - **b.** includes only men.
    - **d.** is loud and rowdy.

Analogies
Analogies Analogies show relationships between pairs of words.

To complete the analogies, decide what kind of relationship is shown by the first pair of words. Then fill in the oval next to the other pair of words that show the same relationship.

1. **bankrupt** is to **wealthy** as
   - **a.** active is to busy
   - **b.** sunny is to clear
   - **c.** healthy is to ill
   - **d.** mischievous is to naughty

2. **obstacle** is to **deter** as
   - **a.** shovel is to rake
   - **b.** gate is to fence
   - **c.** leisure is to work
   - **d.** trap is to entangle

3. **jovial** is to **celebration** as
   - **a.** duty is to voluntary
   - **b.** ingenious is to smart
   - **c.** destructive is to blight
   - **d.** valiant is to coward

4. **perch** is to **bird** as
   - **a.** oven is to heat
   - **b.** crouch is to lion
   - **c.** beat is to rhythm
   - **d.** pigment is to skin

5. **radiant** is to **dim** as
   - **a.** timid is to shy
   - **b.** inept is to clumsy
   - **c.** annoying is to bothersome
   - **d.** fresh is to stale

6. **gully** is to **hill** as
   - **a.** ocean is to desert
   - **b.** valley is to ditch
   - **c.** velocity is to speed
   - **d.** ambiguous is to question

7. **destructive** is to **hurtful** as
   - **a.** physical is to musical
   - **b.** polite is to rude
   - **c.** shiny is to dull
   - **d.** appreciative is to thankful

8. **generate** is to **produce** as
   - **a.** debate is to agree
   - **b.** migrate is to settle
   - **c.** accelerate is to speed up
   - **d.** despise is to love

9. **abominable** is to **pleasant** as
   - **a.** bright is to gloomy
   - **b.** depressed is to sad
   - **c.** posterity is to offspring
   - **d.** weary is to upset

10. **detect** is to **discover** as
    - **a.** find is to keep
    - **b.** climb is to fall
    - **c.** detach is to loosen
    - **d.** mangle is to tie

Games & Activities

Word Volleyball

A game that reinforces vocabulary skills

Prepare for the game by listing the chapter vocabulary words on the board or on a sheet of paper. Divide into two teams and line up in two rows facing one another. Toss a coin to see which team goes first. The winning team begins the game by naming the first vocabulary word on the list. The first person on the opposing team must provide a synonym for the word. Then, as in the game of volleyball, the word is tossed back to the other team. The second person on that team must provide another synonym for the word.

Play continues until one group cannot provide a correct synonym. The team that provides the last correct synonym scores a point. The team that correctly gave the last synonym names the next word on the list, and play continues as before. This game can also be played by using antonyms.

Word Cube

A fun activity that reinforces correct vocabulary usage in written language

Prepare for the game by finding a partner. You will each need a piece of paper, a pencil, tape, and a pair of scissors. Each of you chooses six chapter vocabulary words and makes a Word Cube. To make a Word Cube, draw six squares in a shape like this on a sheet of paper.

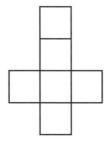

Cut along the outside lines. Write one of the chapter vocabulary words you chose in each square. Then fold and tape the sides of the shape to make a cube. Each partner takes a turn and rolls the cube twice. To score a point, write a sentence that makes sense with the two words that you rolled. The first player to get five points wins the game.

Vocabulary Commercials

A creative dramatics activity that reinforces vocabulary skills

Find three partners. You will need several pieces of paper and a pen or pencil. On one piece of paper list the vocabulary words from your current chapter. Then make a list of things that you use every day—a bowl, cereal, shoes, and so on. Choose one of the items you listed and write a television commercial to advertise that product. Write a script that lets all three partners play a role. Use at least 10 of the vocabulary words from the current chapter in your commercial.

Practice acting out your commercial. Present it for others in your class.

Creating Categories

A fun activity that promotes exploring word meanings and finding connections among words

Find two partners. You will each need a paper and pencil. Write the chapter vocabulary words and their definitions on a sheet of paper. Each partner writes three of the vocabulary words that are related in some way. For example, you might list words that are all used to describe people, are all nouns, or all describe ways to move from place to place. Challenge your partners to guess the connection between the words you listed.

Conducting Interviews

A creative dramatics activity that encourages the application of vocabulary skills

Find a partner. You will need a paper and a pencil. Decide which partner will be the news reporter and which partner will be interviewed. The reporter writes questions to ask in the interview. The questions should contain at least ten of the vocabulary words from the current chapter. The person being interviewed answers the questions, using vocabulary words if possible. When the interview is complete, switch places and let the other partner write questions and conduct an interview.

Crack the Number Code

A fun activity that reinforces vocabulary skills through critical thinking

With a partner, write ten sentences using the current chapter vocabulary words. Next, assign a number to each letter of the alphabet (A=1, B=2, C=3, and so on). Code all the words in your sentences with the numbers you have assigned. For example, the code for the sentence "The cat sat on a mat", would be:

$$20,8,5 + 3,1,20 + 19,1,20 + 15,14 + 1 + 13,1,20$$

Once you have coded all the sentences, exchange papers with another group and try to "crack the code." The first team to correctly "crack the code" wins the game.

Crossword Puzzle

A fun activity that reinforces vocabulary skills

Prepare for the game by bringing crossword puzzles from newspapers or magazines to class. You will need one piece of graph paper and a pencil. Use these examples as a guide to create a crossword puzzle using the current chapter vocabulary words. The word clues for "across" and "down" will be the vocabulary word definitions.

When finished, exchange puzzles with a friend and complete it. Return the crossword puzzle to its owner to check for accuracy.

Vocabulary Board Games

A thinking activity that reinforces vocabulary skills

Find a partner and discuss types of board games that you like to play. Talk about the parts of the game, the rules, and the object of the games, Together with your partner, create a "Vocabulary Board Game." Think of a way to include the vocabulary words in the game. For example, the vocabulary words could be made into word cards for players to define as they land on a certain square on the game board.

Create a game board inside of a manilla folder, find/make up game pieces, and a list of game rules. When finished, play the game or exchange Vocabulary Board Games with classmates. Keep the board games in a designated spot in the classroom and adapt the vocabulary cards for each new vocabulary chapter.

Step Up Vocabulary

An oral language activity to reinforce vocabulary usage

Line up along a line or wall with the rest of your classmates. Place a second line about 15 feet away. Each player in turn must correctly answer a vocabulary related question, such as:

- What is the definition of the vocabulary word?
- Use the vocabulary word correctly in a sentence.
- What is a synonym for this vocabulary word?
- What is an antonym for this vocabulary word?
- What is the root word for this vocabulary word?
- Name three word forms of this vocabulary word?
- What is the present/past/future tense of this word?

If the player correctly answers a question, they may advance one step toward the line, taking a step as big as possible, without jumping. The first player to reach the line is the winner.

All About Alliteration

A fun activity that reinforces correct vocabulary usage

Alliteration is the repetition of initial sounds within a sentence. Use your current vocabulary chapter words to create alliteration sentences. The only words which can be used although they do not start with the initial letter are: *and, in, of, the, a, an.* The object of the game is to see which group can come up with the longest sentence. (It can be silly, but it must make sense.) For example, using the vocabulary word *timid:*

The tremendously <u>timid</u> tiger tossed twelve tasteless trees toward the terrified turtle.

Index

Here is a list of all the words defined in this book. The number following each word indicates the page on which the word is defined. The Challenge Words are listed in *italics*. The Word Study words are listed in **boldface**.